Florida Edition

SCHOLASTIC
READ XL

PRACTICE BOOK >> GRADE 7

PROGRAM CONSULTANTS

Patrick Daley
Publishing Director
Intervention and Middle School
Curriculum, Scholastic Inc.

Sharon Draper
National Teacher of the Year, 1997
Author, Educator, and Consultant
University of Cincinnati
Cincinnati, Ohio

Dr. James Lawson
Senior Director for Curriculum
Orange County Public Schools
Orlando, Florida

Noelle Morris
Language Arts Teacher
Language Arts Department Chair,
Grades 6–8
Corner Lake Middle School
Orlando, Florida

Alfredo Schifini
Professor, School of Education
Division of Curriculum Instruction
California State University
Los Angeles, California

Copyright © 2002, 2001 by Scholastic Inc.   All rights reserved.   Published by Scholastic Inc.   Printed in the U.S.A.

ISBN 0-439-33027-0

1 2 3 4 5 6 7 8 9 10   40   09 08 07 06 05 04 03 02 01

CONTENTS

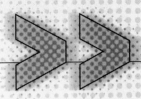

CONTENTS

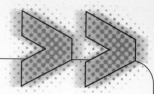

Name _____

Words, Words, Words

> 1 **conviction:** a strong belief in something
> 2 **lingered:** stayed or waited around
> 3 **trudged:** walked slowly with effort
> 4 **sheepishly:** acting in an embarrassed way for having done something foolish
> 5 **sprint:** a fast run for a short distance
> 6 **bulletin:** a short report

>> **A.** Fill in each blank with a word from the box.

On Victor's first day of school, he overslept and made a (1) _____ to the bus stop. The bell rang for first period classes, but Teresa (2) _____ in homeroom to talk to the teacher. Knowing that Teresa was not in his next class, Victor (3) _____ sadly down the hallway. Victor was impressed with Michael's (4) _____ that he knew what would attract girls. Victor stopped to read a (5) _____ posted on the wall. Victor smiled (6) _____ at his own attempt to speak French.

>> **B.** Write four sentences about the life of a seventh grader. Use a different vocabulary word in each sentence.

1. _____

2. _____

3. _____

4. _____

Journal Find three more words in the selection that describe something about school. Write sentences using the words in your journal.

Word Study

LA.A.1.3.3.7.1 Extends the vocabulary-building expectations of the sixth grade using seventh grade or higher vocabulary
LA.A.1.3.2.7.1 Uses knowledge of word parts to determine the meaning of unfamiliar words in a literary or informative text

Name _____

Prefixes

Prefix	Meaning
tri-	three
re-	again, further
un-	not, opposite to

A **prefix** is a letter or a group of letters that appears at the beginning of a word and changes the word's meaning.

>> **A.** Circle the prefix in each word. Draw a line from the word to its meaning.

1. triangle   **a.** not sure

2. review   **b.** a shape with three sides

3. uncertain   **c.** to look at again

4. research   **d.** not friendly

5. unkind   **e.** to explore further

>> **B.** Read each sentence and the words that follow it. Write the word that fits in the blank.

1. Victor wanted to be _____, so he didn't tell Michael that his scowling looked strange. (kind, unkind)

2. The school, gym, and library formed the _____-shaped campus. (angle, triangle)

3. After school, Victor went to the library do so some _____. (search, research)

4. Because he was _____ of the correct answer, Victor mumbled his reply. (certain, uncertain)

5. Before Teresa began her French homework, she _____ her notes from class. (viewed, reviewed)

Journal Look in the newspaper for three words that contain prefixes. Then write the words and their meanings in your journal.

Name _____

Analyze Character

>> **A.** Look again at p. 10 of "Seventh Grade." Gary Soto does more than just tell us how Victor feels about Teresa. He shows us Victor's character through his thoughts, words, and actions. Look at the examples on the chart below. Then add other examples in each category.

> You learn about **characters** in a story through their words, thoughts, and actions.

WORDS

"Yeah, well, I picked up a few things from movies and books. . . ."

THOUGHTS

Victor wished he could start his life over.

ACTIONS

Victor bit his thumb.

>> **B.** Write a sentence telling what you learned about Victor's character from this chart.

_____

_____

Name _____

Cognates

>> **A.** Read the paragraph below. Find and circle five words that look like the Spanish words in the box.

> **Cognates** are words from different languages that have the same meaning and are similar in form.

campo	fruta	plato
convicción	sorpresa	

Victor picked up a tray and a plate, and walked to the end of the cafeteria line on campus. He took a sandwich, cookie, and milk. He also bought a piece of fruit for after school. Victor saw Michael near the window and sat with him. Where was Teresa, Victor wondered. He had the conviction that something good was going to happen. He looked out the window and was surprised to see Teresa sitting under a tree.

>> **B.** Write the circled words next to the correct definitions below.

1. to be amazed or astonished by something not expected   _____

2. a flat dish   _____

3. a strong belief   _____

4. a place where a school is located   _____

5. the part of a flowering plant that contains seeds   _____

⬤ **Activity** Tell a partner about a book, a movie, or a sporting event that you enjoyed. Try to use at least two cognates.

Name _____

Types of Sentences

There are four main types of sentences. A **declarative sentence** makes a statement and ends with a period. An **interrogative sentence** asks a question and ends with a question mark. An **exclamatory sentence** shows strong feeling and ends with an exclamation point. An **imperative sentence** gives an order and ends with a period.

>> A. Read each sentence. Decide which type of sentence it is. Write your answer in the blank.

1. Victor stood in line half an hour. _____

2. How come you're making a face? _____

3. What classes are you taking? _____

4. Talk to Mrs. Gaines. _____

5. She would be a good source of advice on ballet. _____

6. In English they reviewed the parts of speech. _____

7. What is a verb? _____

8. Now tell me what a noun is. _____

9. Teresa is right outside! _____

10. Mr. Bueller shuffled through the papers on his desk. _____

>> B. Write your own declarative, interrogative, imperative, and exclamatory sentences about "Seventh Grade."

1. **Declarative:** _____

2. **Interrogative:** _____

3. **Imperative:** _____

4. **Exclamatory:** _____

Name _____

Sneak Preview

>> Look again at the movie schedule on page 14 of your book as you complete this activity.

Pick one of the movies from the schedule in your book. Imagine what the movie is about. Then use the chart below to organize your ideas about the movie.

> Don't make your plot too complicated. You don't want the audience to get confused.

Movie title: _____

Main characters: **Played by:**

_____   _____

_____   _____

_____   _____

_____   _____

Plot (What happens):

_____

_____

_____

_____

_____

Top 3 reasons to see (or stay away from) this movie:

1. _____

2. _____

3. _____

Name _____

Words, Words, Words

> **urgency:** needing immediate attention
> **adjacent:** close or next to something
> **simultaneously:** happening at the same time
> **precariously:** in an unsafe and risky way
> **anguish:** a strong feeling of sadness and nervousness
> **helmet:** a head covering

>> **A.** Use one of the words from the box to fill in each blank.

Fire fighting is an exciting, but dangerous job. Sometimes firefighters

must balance (1) _____ on a window sill. Luckily, a

(2) _____ can protect a firefighter's head. The firefighters' sense

of (3) _____ helps them act quickly. Many firefighters do several

different jobs (4) _____ to put out a fire. In addition to putting out

a fire, they must take care that the blaze does not jump to (5) _____

buildings. Firefighters understand the (6) _____ people feel when

their home burns down.

>> **B.** Make up sentences using two of the vocabulary words in each sentence.

Word	Word	Sentence
adjacent	anguish	
urgency	simultaneously	
helmet	precariously	

Journal Look for three other words in a newspaper or magazine that describe people helping others. Write them in your journal.

LA.A.1.3.3.7.1 Extends the vocabulary-building expectations of the sixth grade using seventh grade or higher vocabulary
LA.A.1.3.2.7.2 Uses context clues to interpret the meaning of what is read

Name _____

Context Clues

>> **A.** Read each sentence below. Circle the words that help you figure out what the underlined word means.

> To figure out the meaning of a new word, look for **context clues**. Use the words and pictures around the new word to help you understand its meaning.

1. The siren blares as the fire truck rushes to the scene.

2. Working quickly, the paramedics set his broken arm.

3. The weight of my rubber turnout coat makes my shoulder ache.

4. Doctors and nurses in the hospital's ER take care of badly injured patients right away.

5. The ambulance sped down the street, carrying the accident victim towards the hospital.

6. Each emergency forces the paramedics to think and act fast.

>> **B.** Use what you have learned. Draw a line from each word to its meaning.

1. siren   **a.** firefighter's protective rubber coat

2. paramedics   **b.** a situation that calls for action right away

3. turnout coat   **c.** something that makes a loud warning sound

4. emergency   **d.** people who are trained to give first aid

5. ambulance   **e.** emergency room, where seriously injured people are brought

6. ER   **f.** vehicle that rushes people to the hospital

Journal Many careers and activities such as computer programming, dance, or football have special vocabularies. Write the name of a career or activity in your journal. Then write three special vocabulary words and their meanings.

Fighting Fire

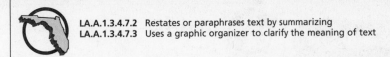

Name _____

Sequence of Events

>> **A.** Reread "Fighting Fire." Then read the list of events below. Write them in the chart in the correct order. The first one is done for you.

She promises to rescue the child.

The fire truck arrives at the scene.

Caroline Paul falls through the roof.

The firefighters go into the burning house.

The alarm comes in around midnight.

> A **sequence of events** is the order in which the events in a story happen. Finding clues and time-order words, such as *next* and *then*, can help you keep track of events.

Event 1: The alarm comes in around midnight.

⇩

Event 2:

⇩

Event 3:

⇩

Event 4:

⇩

Event 5:

Fighting Fire

7

ESL/Language Support

LA.D.2.3.1.7.1 Uses words and images that best express intended messages

Name _____

Words That Describe Speaking

>> **A.** Read the dialogue. Circle the words that are synonyms for *said* or *say*.

> A **synonym** is a word that has the same or similar meaning as another word. To vary their writing and show how characters talk, writers use different synonyms for *said* or *say*. Examples are: *answers, mutters, hisses, yells,* and *tells*.

1. "Quick! Get the fire hose up here!" Caroline yells from the top of the staircase.

2. "I need a hand. The hose is caught on a piece of furniture," William answers.

3. Caroline looks down, sees him struggling, and hisses, "Why does this have to happen?"

4. "Come on, come on," William muttered as he struggled with the fire hose.

5. "I'm coming down to help you," Caroline told William.

>> **B.** Fill in the blanks with synonyms for *said*. Use the words in the box or your own synonyms for *said*.

1. "Call an ambulance! I just saw a car accident!" _____ Mark.

2. "Where did it happen?" _____ the storekeeper.

3. "On the corner of Ninth Street and Woodson," Mark _____ him.

4. "Ninth and Woodson," the storekeeper _____ to himself as he dials.

5. "Stay back," _____ a police officer, who has already arrived at the scene of the accident.

Activity With a partner, talk about a conversation you overheard. Try to use two different words for *said*.

Name _____

Adverbs Ending in -*ly*

> An **adverb** is a word that describes a verb, an adjective, or another adverb. Some adverbs tell when, where, or how the action happens. Many adverbs end in –*ly*. Examples: *swiftly, happily.*

>> **A.** Underline the adverb ending in -*ly* in each sentence. Then rewrite the sentence using a different adverb from the box below.

> loudly   quietly   silently
>
> calmly   steadily

1. A fire alarm rings suddenly.

_____

2. The firefighters quickly reach for their coats and helmets.

_____

3. Abruptly, the fire truck screeches to a stop.

_____

4. The firefighters work together perfectly.

_____

5. Paramedics work quickly.

_____

>> **B.** Write three sentences of your own using the adverbs in parentheses ( ).

1. (carefully) _____

2. (thoughtfully) _____

3. (clearly) _____

Name _____

Make a Plan

>> Look again at the medicine labels on page 24 of your book as you complete this activity.

Imagine that your doctor wants you to take Claritox.
Reread the label. Then use this chart to plan a schedule for taking your medicine.
Tell when you will eat and when you will take your medicine.

> Be sure to read all the labels and warning stickers on a medicine bottle.

Day	Dose Number	Time of Meal	Time to Take Medicine
Friday	1		
	2		
	3		
Saturday			
Sunday			
Monday			

Vocabulary

 LA.A.1.3.3.7.1 Extends the vocabulary-building expectations of the sixth grade using seventh grade or higher vocabulary

Name _____

Words, Words, Words

frugal: careful not to waste money

considered: believed that something is true

remarks: comments about something

realistic: concerned with the way things really are

opportunity: a chance to do something

advice: suggestions for improvement

>> **A.** Fill in the blanks with words from the box. Then read the circled letters going down. You'll find out what to call someone who helps you make a difficult decision.

1. careful about money   f r u g a l

2. believed something is true   c o n s i d e r e d

3. concerning the way things are r e a l i s t i c

4. comments   r e m a r k s

5. a chance   o p p o r t u n i t y

6. suggestions for improving   a d v i c e

>> **B.** Write a sentence of your own using these vocabulary words:

1. remarks _____

_____

2. realistic _____

_____

3. opportunity _____

_____

Journal Look for three other words in your book that might be used in a paragraph about making hard decisions. Write them in your journal.

Name _____

Figurative Language

> **A.** Read each figurative language phrase. Write **simile** or **metaphor** on the line. The first one is done for you.

> **Figurative language** is a special use of words that helps readers picture what is being described.
> **Simile:** a comparison that uses the word *like* or *as*.
> **Metaphor:** a comparison in which one thing is said to be another.

1. like a hawk _____simile_____

2. They were all eyes _____

3. like a fortune in diamonds _____

4. He seemed to fold up into a tiny gray package _____

5. Was Terrence a pigeon? _____

6. greedy as a wolf _____

> **B.** Rewrite each sentence. Replace the underlined words with figurative language from the exercise above. The first one is done for you.

1. They were <u>watching with wide eyes</u>.

They were all eyes. _____

2. Mr. Watts <u>looked sad and shrunken</u>.

_____

3. Mr. Watts watched her <u>closely and carefully</u> as she pumped the gas.

_____

4. The cat hadn't eaten in days and was <u>eating as much as it could</u>.

_____

📖 **Journal** Look through a short story, novel, or poem for other examples of figurative language. Write several expressions and their meanings in your journal.

LA.A.1.3.4.7.3 Uses a graphic organizer to clarify the meaning of text
LA.A.2.3.1.7.1 Extends the expectations of the sixth grade with increasingly complex reading texts and assignments and tasks

Name _____

Draw Conclusions

> When you **draw a conclusion** you make a judgment or decision based on information that you've read plus your own experience.

>> **A.** Read the facts on the chart about "Only a Dollar's Worth." Then write a conclusion based on them in the box.

Fact:	Fact:
When Mr. Watts returned, Isabel noticed the torn upholstery inside the car.	Isabel pretended to find the lost $20 in the back seat.
Conclusion:	
_____	
_____	
_____	

>> **B.** Make your own Drawing Conclusions chart for "Just a Pigeon." Include these facts: Fact: Terrence was saving his money to go to college. Fact: He used his money to take a wounded pigeon to a vet. Then draw a conclusion about Terrence.

>> **C.** Make your own Drawing Conclusions chart for "A Matter of Honor." Include these facts: Fact: Tina saw her best friend cheat on a test. Fact: The class was on an honor system. Draw a conclusion about how Tina felt.

Name _____

Irregular Verbs

paid	found	felt
held	thought	took
said	stole	stood

> Most verbs in English form the past tense by adding *-d* or *-ed*. But some verbs are **irregular**, and the past tense of many of these verbs change their spelling *(pay/paid)*.

>> A. Read these sentences aloud. Find the correct **past-tense** form of each underlined verb in the box above. Then write it on the line. The first one has been done for you.

1. Carlos <u>feels</u> happy about winning the game. _____felt_____

2. I <u>think</u> the movie was funny. _____

3. Who <u>says</u> the music is too loud? _____

4. She always <u>pays</u> her share. _____

5. Adriana <u>finds</u> friends all over the world. _____

>> B. Write your own sentences using the past tense of five **irregular verbs**.

1. _____

2. _____

3. _____

4. _____

5. _____

Activity Tell a partner what you did yesterday after school. Use two irregular past-tense verbs.

Name _____

Linking Verbs

>> **A.** Underline the linking verb in each sentence. Draw an arrow between the words it connects. The first one is done for you.

> A **linking verb** shows a state of being rather than an action. A linking verb links, or connects, the subject of a sentence with a word or words in the predicate.
>
> **Linking Verbs:**
>
> | | | |
> |---|---|---|
> | am | are | is |
> | was | were | will be |
> | look | feel | sound |
> | taste | smell | seem |

1. Suddenly, Mr. Watts seemed old.

2. The old man was speechless.

3. Isabel felt sorry for him.

4. Does the lemon taste sour?

5. They looked strong and proud.

>> **B.** Complete each sentence with a linking verb. Choose from the verbs listed in the box.

1. The back seat of the car _____ shabby.

2. Terrence _____ good about helping the pigeon.

3. Tina _____ unhappy with Rachel.

4. His cough _____ bad.

5. The pies on the window sill _____ delicious.

>> **C.** Write your own sentences using the linking verb in parentheses ( ).

1. (is) _____

2. (were) _____

3. (smell) _____

LA.A.2.3.5.7.2 Compiles, organizes, and interprets information for a variety of purposes

Name _____

Top Jobs

>> Look again at the job application on page 36 of your book as you complete this activity.

List three summer jobs that you would love to have. What skills and experiences would these jobs require? Write down your ideas in the chart below.

Think about what jobs will let you develop your skills and explore your interests.

Job	What skills and experiences would this job require?	Which of these skills and experiences do you have?

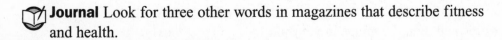

LA.A.1.3.2.7.2 Uses context clues to interpret the meaning of what is read

Name _____

Words, Words, Words

> **reasonable:** fair
>
> **improve:** to make better
>
> **concentrated:** focused your thoughts and attention on something
>
> **discouraged:** caused to give up hope or confidence
>
> **emotions:** strong feelings of any kind
>
> **fitness:** the state of being physically fit

>> A. Complete each sentence by writing one of the words from the box in the blank.

1. I wanted to _____ my appearance by getting fit.

2. I worked out at the gym and always tried to be home at a _____ hour.

3. At first I was very _____ because I didn't notice any difference in the way I looked.

4. I wanted to be able to do more pull-ups, so I _____ on strengthening my arms.

5. My _____ were so overwhelming I almost cried when I began to see results.

6. Finally, I was in shape and had achieved total _____.

>> B. Use five of the words above in sentences to describe gym class.

1. _____

2. _____

3. _____

4. _____

5. _____

Journal Look for three other words in magazines that describe fitness and health.

Word Study

LA.A.1.3.2.7.1 Uses knowledge of word parts to determine the meaning of unfamiliar words in literary or informative text

Name _____

Roots

>> **A.** Use the common roots in the box to figure out the meaning of the underlined word. Then write the meaning in the space provided.

> A **root** is a word or word part from Latin or another language that is the basis of an English word. By knowing a root's meaning, you can often figure out the meaning of a word in which it appears.

Root	Meaning
pop	people
spec	view, see
semi	half
vict	conquer

1. He was an extremely <u>popular</u> soccer player because he scored so many goals.

_____

2. She wanted to <u>inspect</u> the gym's equipment before joining it.

_____

3. The team's <u>victory</u> made everyone happy.

_____

4. Her favorite treat is <u>semi-sweet</u> chocolate.

_____

>> **B.** Write three original sentences about *Confessions of a Gym-Class Dropout.* Each sentence should contain a word with one of the roots above.

1. _____

2. _____

3. _____

Journal Look for other words in magazines that contain the roots in the box above. Try to determine what each of these words means. Then write the words and their meanings in your journal.

LA.A.1.3.4.7.3 Uses a graphic organizer to clarify the meaning of text
LA.A.2.3.1.7.1 Extends the expectations of the sixth grade with increasingly complex reading texts and assignments and tasks

Name _____

Analyze Plot

>> Complete the chart to analyze plot for Scene Eight of *Confessions of a Gym-Class Dropout*.

> A **plot** is the series of events that takes place in a story. The plot usually focuses on a problem the main character faces and is trying to solve.

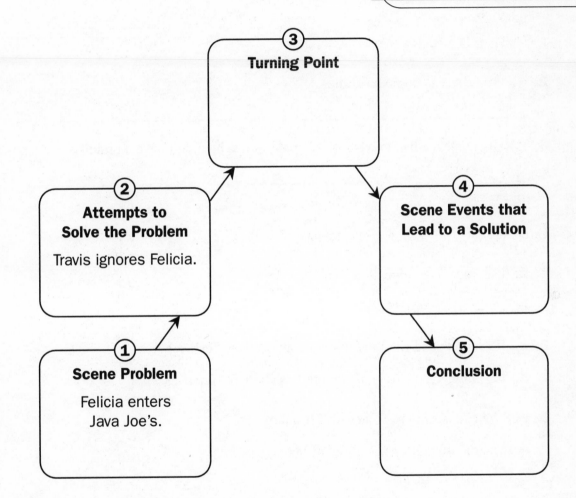

③ Turning Point

② Attempts to Solve the Problem

Travis ignores Felicia.

④ Scene Events that Lead to a Solution

① Scene Problem

Felicia enters Java Joe's.

⑤ Conclusion

Confessions of a Gym Class Dropout

Name _____

Sarcastic Tone

>> **A.** Find these sarcastic expressions in the selection. Rewrite them so they no longer have a sarcastic tone.

> A **sarcastic tone** is one that uses words to make fun of someone or something. Sarcastic expressions often say the opposite of what they really mean.

1. In fact, Travis is the Schwarzenegger of couch potatoes.

_____

2. It's the sweetest couple on earth.

_____

3. But of course, he had to work on his body, since he didn't have a brain.

_____

>> **B.** Circle the sarcastic sentence in each pair.

1. a. I scored a goal. Great!

　b. I missed the goal. Great!

2. a. It's raining and I left my umbrella at the gym. Terrific!

　b. It's raining and I have my umbrella right here. Terrific!

3. a. The fire alarm just went off. Get out of here.

　b. You did 40 pull-ups? Get out of here.

● **Activity** Write a comic strip about a gym class using two expressions on this page.

Name _____

Consistent Verb Tenses

> A **verb tense** signals the time of the action—past, present, or future. Good writers maintain a consistent tense throughout to avoid confusing readers.

>> **A.** Read each sentence and circle the tense of the underlined verb.

1. The gym teacher <u>makes</u> fun of Travis.

    Past   Present   Future

2. Rocco <u>finished</u> his exercises earlier that day.

    Past   Present   Future

3. Travis <u>decides</u> to get in shape.

    Past   Present   Future

4. The teacher <u>will be</u> happy with Travis.

    Past   Present   Future

5. Then Travis <u>will tie</u> Rocco at pull-ups.

    Past   Present   Future

>> **B.** Each sentence has a blank followed by two verb choices. Circle the verb that is consistent in tense with the underlined verb in the first sentence.

The girls <u>entered</u> the gym. Jane (1) _____ (dribbles, dribbled) the ball

across the court. Then Ellen (2)_____(jumped, jumps) in front of Jane.

Jane (3) _____ (tries, tried) to make a shot. Swish! The basketball

(4) _____ (glided, glides) through the hoop.

Name _____

Plan a Trip

>> Look again at the map on page 50 of your book as you complete this activity.

Use the scale of miles to help you measure the distances between places.

Plan a two-day visit to Washington, D.C. Make a list of the sights you will visit each day, in the order you will visit them. Plan your trip so that you will spend as little time as possible going from one place to the next.

Day One	Day Two

Confessions of a Gym Class Dropout

Name _____

Words, Words, Words

> **allergic:** reacting to something by sneezing, coughing or breaking out in a rash
> **furiously:** intensely or fiercely
> **suspicious:** feeling as if something is wrong with little or no proof
> **distract:** to weaken a person's concentration
> **rancid:** spoiled
> **protected:** guarded against harm

>> **A.** Find the missing words. Fill in each blank with a word from the box.

"Shelly, the old sea turtle must be (1) _____ from danger," thought

Berin, "but how?" Berin knew he would have to (2) _____ the turtle

hunters long enough for Shelly to lay her eggs and swim away. What could he do

that would not make the turtle hunters (3) _____?

Berin walked along his favorite beach, thinking and kicking the

(4) _____, smelly seaweed along the shore. He sat down near some

beach grass and sneezed. "I must be (5) _____ to beach grass," he

thought. He walked away from the beach grass, scratching his arm. By the time he

got home, he was (6) _____ scratching the rash on his arm.

>> **B.** Draw a line from each word to the phrase that fits it.

1. rancid	**a.** what endangered species are
2. protected	**b.** what spoiled meat is
3. suspicious	**c.** why people sneeze around pollen
4. furiously	**d.** what a detective is
5. allergic	**e.** in a way that is intense or fierce

Journal Look for three words in a newspaper or magazine about
animals. Write them in your journal.

Smelly Feat

LA.A.1.3.3.7.1 Extends the vocabulary-building expectations of the sixth grade using seventh grade or higher vocabulary
LA.A.1.3.2.7.1 Uses knowledge of word parts to determine the meaning of unfamiliar words in a literary or informative text

Name _____

Multiple Prefixes and Suffixes

Prefixes		Suffixes/Endings	
ab-	away from, not	**-ful**	full of
in-	in, not, within	**-ing**	in the process of
un-	not	**-ly**	done in a way, like

A **prefix** is a letter or group of letters at the beginning of a word that changes its meaning. A **suffix** is a group of letters at the end of a word that changes its meaning and its part of speech. Some words have more than one prefix and suffix.

>> A. Look at the meaning of the prefixes and suffixes/endings in the chart. Then read the words below. Underline the prefix and/or suffix/endings in each word. Draw a line from the word to its meaning.

1. abnormally   **a.** not in a direct way

2. indirectly   **b.** not done in a usual way

3. painfully   **c.** not being deserving of something

4. unhappily   **d.** not in a joyous way

5. undeserving   **e.** done in a way that is full of hurt

>> B. Read each item. Circle the word that fits in the blank.

1. Turtle Island was not near the hill. It lay _____ behind it. **(directly, indirectly)**

2. The noisy island was_____ quiet that day. **(abnormally, normally)**

3. Berin was _____ of an award for helping Old Shelly. **(undeserving, deserving)**

Journal Look for three more words in the selection that contain one or more prefixes and or suffixes. Write your own definitions. Then look the words up in a dictionary, and add the dictionary definitions to your journal.

     Smelly Feat

LA.A.1.3.4.7.3 Uses a graphic organizer to clarify the meaning of text
LA.A.2.3.1.7.1 Extends the expectations of the sixth grade with increasingly complex reading texts and assignments and tasks

Name _____

Problem and Solution

▶▶ How does Berin save Shelly from Horse and his gang? Complete the graphic organizer below.

> A **problem** is something that a story character must solve.
> A **solution** is the way the character figures out the answer to the problem.

PROBLEM 1

How can Berin save Old Shelly from Horse and his gang?

Attempt:

Solution:

PROBLEM 2

Horse and his gang are not in school on the day Old Shelly comes ashore. So, Berin must figure out how to leave school early.

Attempt:

Solution:

Smelly Feat

Name _____

Exaggeration

>> **A.** Draw a line from the exaggeration in the first column to the more literal expression it matches in the second column.

> **Exaggeration** is used to make things seem larger than life. We often use it for humor or emphasis.

1. This heat is killing me.

2. I could eat a bear.

3. He howled like a wolf.

4. This desk is harder to move than a mountain.

5. It took me forever to do my math.

a. I'm really hungry.

b. It took me a long time to do my math.

c. It's very hot.

d. He yelled.

e. The desk is very heavy.

>> **B.** Write your own exaggerated version of the statements below.

1. I'm tired. _____

_____

2. You're late! _____

_____

3. He's so tall! _____

_____

⬤ **Activity** Tell a funny story to a partner. Use at least two exaggerations to make the actions and descriptions more humorous.

LA.D.1.3.1.7.1 Identifies patterns and rules found in the English language

Name _____

Compound Sentences

> A **compound sentence** is a sentence made up of two simple sentences joined by a comma and the word *or, and,* or *but.*

>> A. Underline the two simple sentences that make up each compound sentence. Then circle the conjunction, or joining word (**and**, **but**, or **or**). The first one is done for you.

1. Old Shelly buried her eggs, (and) then she crawled back into the sea.

2. Some animals must be protected, but others are doing very well.

3. Keisha can travel to Alaska to study bears, or she can go to Florida to study alligators.

4. You can write an article about the sea turtles, and I can illustrate it.

>> B. Fill in the blanks with **and, but,** or **or**.

1. Do you want pizza, _____ would you rather have hamburgers?

2. I went to buy a ticket, _____ the concert was sold out.

3. My cousin visited me, _____ I took him to a soccer game.

>> C. Write three compound sentences about something you did with a friend or family member. Use the words shown.

1. and: _____

_____

2. or: _____

_____

3. but: _____

_____

Smelly Feat

LA.A.2.3.8.7.4 Identifies the influences of personal values on the conclusions an author draws
LA.A.2.3.3.7.1 Identifies persuasive and propaganda techniques in text
LA.A.2.3.3.7.2 Delineates the strengths and weaknesses of an argument

Name _____

Analyze It

>> Look again at the cartoon on page 66
of your book as you complete this activity.

Find an editorial cartoon in a newspaper. Read it
closely. What do you think the cartoonist is saying?
Do you agree? Write your ideas in the chart below.

> Remember to use all of the clues in the cartoon and the caption to help you understand the cartoonist's message.

What's the cartoon about?	What is the cartoonist's message?	Do you agree or disagree?

Name _____

Words, Words, Words

> **illegal:** against the law
>
> **justice:** fair treatment
>
> **campaign:** actions that lead to something important
>
> **opponents:** people who fight against a cause or person
>
> **convert:** to make something into something else
>
> **enslave:** to make someone a slave

>> A. Solve the puzzle with words from the box.

Across

1. people fighting against something

3. actions taken to achieve a specific goal

5. fair treatment

Down

2. to force someone to be a slave

4. not legal

6. to change something into something else

Crossword solution:

- 1 Across: o p p o n e n t s
- 2 Down: e n s l a v e
- 3 Across: c a m p a i g n
- 4 Down: i l l e g a l
- 5 Across: j u s t i c e
- 6 Down: c o n v e r t

>> B. What issues do you feel strongly about? Write sentences of your own using three vocabulary words.

1. _____

2. _____

3. _____

Journal Find three other words in the selection that have to do with fighting for a cause. Write them in your journal.

Name _____

Contractions

> A **contraction** is a shortened form of two words. The apostrophe represents the missing letter or letters.

Contractions with:

not	is	are	had	have
didn't	she's	they're	I'd	I've
wasn't	he's	we're	they'd	they've
isn't	it's	you're	he'd	we've
couldn't				

>> **A.** Underline the contraction in each sentence. On the line, write the two words that form the contraction. The first one is done for you.

1. Weren't you inspired by the story of Iqbal Masih? _____were not_____

2. He had a short life, but he'd done important work. _____

3. Iqbal didn't have rich parents. _____

4. He worked hard, but couldn't pay off the debt. _____

5. They've built a school in Iqbal's honor. _____

>> **B.** Write the contraction on the line. Use the words in parentheses ( ).

1. (They had) _____ sold their child for a small sum of money.

2. (It is) _____ time such practices were stopped.

3. (I have) _____ seen photographs of children working in factories.

4. I (do not) _____ know how their little bodies worked so hard.

5. (They have) _____ formed a partnership with a local group.

Journal Look for contractions as you read. Write them in your journal. Next to each one, write the two words that form the contraction. Use a dictionary for help if you need it.

Name _____

Compare and Contrast

>> **A.** Compare and contrast the lives of Iqbal Masih and Wendy Diaz. Complete the sentences in each circle of the chart. Then add another difference and a similarity for each.

To **compare** things means to show how things are alike. To **contrast** means to find differences. You can compare or contrast people, places, objects, and ideas.

DIFFERENT
Iqbal

1. He lived in _____

2. He worked in _____

3. He risked his life to _____

4. _____

SAME

9. Both spoke out **against** _____

10. _____

DIFFERENT
Wendy

5. She lives in _____

6. She worked in _____

7. She was brought to the U.S. to _____

8. _____

Iqbal Masih: Crusader for Children

Name _____

Past-Tense Verbs

traced	hoped	laced
hiked	taped	filed
saved	biked	raced

> To form the **past tense** of most verbs ending in *e*, drop the *e* and add *-ed*.

>> **A.** Read these sentences aloud. Then change the underlined past-tense verb to the present tense and write it on the line.

1. I <u>raced</u> to my class in astronomy. _____

2. They <u>hiked</u> in the hills every weekend. _____

3. We <u>hoped</u> to return to the shore next year. _____

4. My brothers <u>saved</u> a lot of money. _____

5. We <u>taped</u> a lot of old movies. _____

>> **B.** Write your own sentences using four past-tense verbs that end in *-ed*.

1. _____

2. _____

3. _____

4. _____

Activity Tell a partner about something that happened last summer. Use three past-tense verbs that end in *-ed*.

Name _____

Adjectives and Adverbs

An **adjective** describes a noun or pronoun. An adjective tells *which, what kind, how many,* or *how much.*
An **adverb** describes a verb, adjective, or other adverb. An adverb tells *how, when, where,* or *to what extent.* Many adverbs end in *-ly.*

>> **A.** Read each sentence. If the underlined word is an adjective, write *ADJ*. If it is an adverb, write *ADV*. Circle the word each adjective or adverb describes. The first one has been done for you.

1. He worked under painful (conditions). ___ADJ___

2. Young Iqbal bravely ran away to be free. _____

3. The factory was horribly crowded. _____

4. Iqbal was paid only pennies a day. _____

>> **B.** Read each sentence. Circle the question the underlined words answer.

1. Iqbal Masih was a child laborer.

What kind?   How many?   Which?

2. He often worked long hours.

What kind?   When?   Which?

3. The factory owner treated him cruelly.

How?   When?   Where?

4. Iqbal fought for decent conditions.

How?   What kind?   Where?

>> **C.** Write two sentences of your own. Use an adjective or adverb that answers the question in parentheses ( ).

1. (How many?) _____

2. (How?) _____

Name _____

Getting Into Print

>> Look again at the letters to the editor on page 76 of your book as you complete this activity.

Turn to the "Letters to the Editor" page in a magazine. Find one positive letter about an article. Find one negative one about the same article. What are the main ideas of each letter? Do you agree or disagree with the writers?

> Use the table of contents in a magazine to find the "letters to the editor" page.

Writer	Letter #1	Letter #2
What is the name of the article the writer is talking about?		
What is the issue date in which the article appeared?		
Is this a positive or negative letter?		
What are the main ideas of the letter?		
Do you agree or disagree with this letter? Why?		

Name _____

Words, Words, Words

> **segregated:** separated
> **taunts:** mean and insulting remarks
> **established:** experienced
> **mediocre:** less than average quality
> **restricted:** stopped from doing something
> **ensured:** made sure

➤➤ **A.** Can you find the missing words? Fill in each blank with a word from the box.

In America in the 1940s and 1950s, there was a social and legal system that

(1) _____ people by the color of their skin. Black people suffered

insults and (2) _____ by whites. They were (3) _____

from going to many whites-only public places. Public facilities for black people-only

were often (4) _____ at best. These conditions (5) _____

that black people did not have the same rights as white people. There were more

(6) _____ black ballplayers than Jackie Robinson in the mid-1940s,

but none had the chance to affect race relations the way he did.

➤➤ **B.** Write three sentences about Jackie Robinson, using one vocabulary word in each.

1. _____

2. _____

3. _____

Journal Find three sports related words in the newspaper. Look up their
meanings, if necessary. Record them in your journal.

Name _____

Compound Words

>> **A.** Read the compound words in the box. Then use them to fill in the blanks in the sentences below.

> A **compound word** is made up of two smaller words. Use the meanings of the two smaller words to help figure out the meaning of the compound.

football	classmates	shortstop	grandson	bathrooms

1. Jackie's _____ wanted him on their school teams.

2. Jackie Robinson was a high school _____ star.

3. Born in Georgia, Robinson was the _____ of a slave.

4. Robinson played _____ for the Kansas City Monarchs.

5. Once there were separate water fountains and _____ for blacks and whites.

>> **B.** Draw a line from one single word to another to make compound words. Write the new word on the line.

1. book   **a.** glasses   **1.** _____

2. eye   **b.** father   **2.** _____

3. gold   **c.** fish   **3.** _____

4. grand   **d.** case   **4.** _____

Write a sentence for each compound word.

5. _____

6. _____

7. _____

8. _____

Journal Look for three more compound words in the selection. Write them in your journal.

The Man Who Changed America

LA.A.1.3.4.7.3 Uses a graphic organizer to clarify the meaning of text
LA.A.2.3.1.7.1 Extends the expectations of the sixth grade with increasingly complex reading texts and assignments and tasks

Name _____

Main Idea

>> **A.** Read the second paragraph in this selection.
Then add details to the Main Idea chart below.

> The **main idea** is the most important idea in a text. Supporting details back up the main idea.

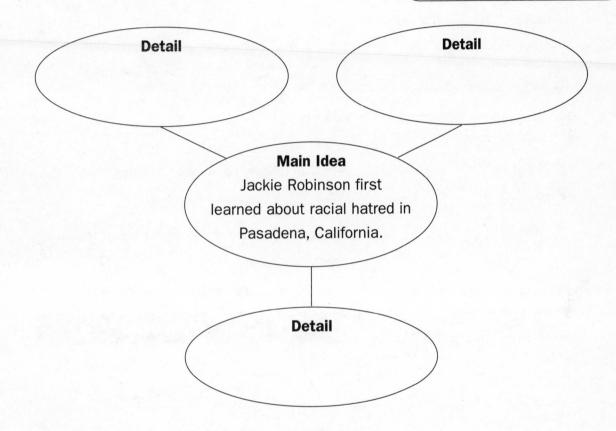

Detail

Detail

Main Idea
Jackie Robinson first learned about racial hatred in Pasadena, California.

Detail

>> **B.** Read the next paragraph: "A Four-Sport Star." The main idea is: Jackie Robinson was always a good athlete. Find three details that support the main idea.

1. _____

2. _____

3. _____

Name _____

Irregular Verbs

>> **A.** Read the irregular verbs in the box. Then fill in the blanks with the past tense of the verbs.

> Most verbs form the **past tense** by adding -d or -ed to the end of the word. **Irregular verbs** don't. Some irregular verbs change their spelling (make/made). Others keep the same spelling (set/set).

> **make   read   do   throw   steal**

1. Jackie Robinson _____ any sport he played look easy.

2. When the Robinsons moved to Pasadena, a man _____ stones at them.

3. What Jackie Robinson _____ inspired all black athletes.

4. Robinson _____ third base every chance he could.

5. Yesterday, I _____ a magazine article about the history of baseball.

>> **B.** Read each word on the chart, then write the past tense of the word in the chart.

Present tense	Past tense
set	
speak	
feel	
sit	
see	

⬤ **Activity** Tell a partner about something that happened yesterday. Use at least two of the irregular past-tense verbs above.

Name _____

Subject and Object Pronouns

> A **subject pronoun** tells who or what performs the action of a sentence. Subject pronouns include *I, you, he, she, it, we, they.* An **object pronoun** tells who or what receives the action. Object pronouns include *me, you, him, her, it, us, them.*

>> **A.** Underline the subject pronouns in each sentence.

1. He wanted Jackie in the major leagues.
2. They were not allowed in the major leagues.
3. He would do anything to get on base.
4. In 1947, I was named Rookie of the Year.
5. We must treat all people with respect.

>> **B.** Write the correct object pronoun to complete each sentence from the list below.

> him   her   me   us   them   you   it

1. Mr. Rickey gave _____ a chance to play for the Brooklyn Dodgers.

2. Robinson said, "Some players slid into _____ with their sharp spikes."

3. Robinson praised his wife whenever he spoke of _____.

4. Black kids looked at Robinson and thought, he is one of _____.

5. Pee Wee Reese said to Robinson, "Look! White fans cheered for

   _____, too."

>> **C.** Write two sentences that include both a subject and object pronoun.

1. _____

2. _____

Name _____

Record Stats

>> Look again at the stats on page 86 of your book as you complete this activity.

When reading the sports stats remember to look at only one line at a time.

Watch a basketball game. Track one player's stats. Each time your player makes a field goal, free throw, three-pointer, or rebound, add a check to the chart below. At the end of the game, add up the stats. Check your records against the official box scores in the newspaper. How did you do?

Player																			Your Score	Official Score
FG																				
3P																				
FT																				
RB																				

FG = Field Goal (worth 2 points)

3P = Three-point Field Goal (worth 3 points)

FT = Free Throw (worth 1 point)

RB = Rebounds

Name _____

Words, Words, Words

> **redefining:** giving new meaning to
>
> **merged:** joined together
>
> **strides:** gains or improvements
>
> **impact:** a strong effect
>
> **acceptance:** feeling like you belong
>
> **cultural:** relating to a culture or group of people

>> A. Use words from the box to fill in the blanks below.

1. You offer this to someone who is new to a group. _____

2. This is the result of a large cause. _____

3. This kind of event is about a particular group's heritage. _____

4. These are positive steps or improvements. _____

5. This is what two things do when they've blended together. _____

6. This happens when something gains a new meaning. _____

>> B. Now write three questions of your own to ask a favorite music star. Use one vocabulary word in each question.

1. _____

2. _____

3. _____

Journal Find three words in a magazine that describe a cultural event. Write them in your journal.

LA.A.1.3.2.7.1 Uses knowledge of word parts to determine the meaning of unfamiliar words in a literary or informative text
LA.A.1.3.3.7.1 Extends the vocabulary-building expectations of the sixth grade using seventh grade or higher vocabulary

Name _____

Suffixes

A **suffix** is a word part added to the end of a word. A suffix can change the part of speech of the original word.

Suffix	Meaning	Part of Speech	Base Word + suffix
-ist	a person who does something	noun	novel + ist = novelist
-ment	the act or result of	noun	achieve + ment = achievement
-ial	relating to	adjective	president + ial = presidential

>> **A.** Read each word. Draw a line between the base word and the suffix. Write the meaning of the whole word.

1. accomplishment _____

2. realist _____

3. presidential _____

4. artist _____

5. astonishment _____

>> **B.** Add the suffix -ment, -ist, or -ial to the base word in parentheses to complete each sentence. Write the new word on the line.

1. Latinos influence _____ elections in the United States. **(president)**

2. That's a smile of _____ on his face. **(content)**

3. I want to be a _____ for Gloria Estefan. **(guitar)**

Journal Find three words with different suffixes in the selection. Write these words in your journal. Underline the suffixes.

LA.A.1.3.4.7.3 Uses a graphic organizer to clarify the meaning of text

Name _____

Read for Detail

> **A.** Fill in the chart with details about the Latino contributions and impact on American culture.

Details are facts or bits of information about a topic.

Latino contributions in American culture

The Latino New Wave

LA.D.1.3.1.7.1 Identifies patterns and rules found in the English language

Name _____

Action Words

> An **action word** tells what the subject of the sentence does. Action words are verbs.

>> A. Circle the action word in each sentence.

1. The crowds danced all night.
2. Ricky Martin sings to a group of his fans.
3. Baseball fans cheered Sammy Sosa's home run.
4. Yxta Maya Murray writes novels.
5. Astronaut Ellen Ochoa flies space-shuttle missions.

>> B. Read the sentences. Fill in the blank with an action word from the box.

> welcomes   paint   overtake
>
> delivers   works

1. Artists _____ murals on building walls.
2. Julio _____ meals to people who can't go out.
3. Maria _____ on weekends.
4. The mayor of the city _____ the visitors.
5. Did salsa _____ ketchup in popularity?

⬡ **Activity** Tell a partner about something you did yesterday. Have your partner record all your action words. Then switch roles. Compare lists of action words.

LA.D.1.3.1.7.1   Identifies patterns and rules found in the English language

Name _____

Main and Helping Verbs

> A main verb shows the main action or state of being of a sentence.
> A helping verb such as *are*, *had*, or *will* works with the main verb. Helping verbs help show when the action or state of being occurs: *present*, *past*, or *future*.

>> A. Underline the main verb and circle the helping verb in each sentence. On the line, write *present*, *past*, or *future* to identify when the action takes place. The first sentence has been done.

1. The singers (had) influenced pop

   music. _____past_____

2. They are going to Ricky Martin's concert. _____

3. We will dance all night long. _____

4. Sammy Sosa had hit more than 60 home runs. _____

5. I will read Gary Soto's new book. _____

>> B. Use a helping verb from the box to complete each sentence.

(are   will   had)

1. In the future, a Latina _____ become president.

2. The mix of cultures _____ created a new type of music.

3. Latino foods _____ making shopping more interesting.

>> C. Write two sentences about the Latin New Wave that include helping verbs.

_____

_____

Name _____

Take a Survey

>> Look again at the pie chart on page 98 of your book as you complete this activity.

Survey ten kids in your class. Ask them what their favorite type of music is. Give them the same choices that appear on this chart. Use this chart to record the students' answers.

> When you survey someone, ask a specific question. Remember each student surveyed can choose only one favorite type of music.

Top Choices

Students	Rhythm and Blues	Country	Pop	Rap/ Hip-Hop	Alternative/ Rock	Classical	Other
1							
2							
3							
4							
5							
6							
7							
8							
9							
10							
Total							

Name _____

Words, Words, Words

> **decent:** thoughtful or kind
>
> **encourages:** shows approval for one's actions
>
> **dissect:** to cut apart a human body in order to examine it
>
> **anxiously:** with worry
>
> **foolproof:** something that cannot fail
>
> **analysis:** the careful examination of something to study it

>> A. Complete each sentence with a word from the box. Write the word on the blank.

1. The students' laughter _____ Mr. Harwood to keep teasing Jordie.

2. Jordie felt sure that his plan was _____ and would scare his classmates.

3. Jordie picked up a scalpel and pretended he was going to _____ the corpse.

4. Mr. Harwood was tough on Jordie's _____ of the compound in his test tube.

5. Marvin looked worried and _____ kept trying to tell Jordie something.

6. He thought she was the only _____ person in the classroom because she didn't make fun of him.

>> B. What would you like to ask a scientist? Write three questions. Use one vocabulary word in each question.

1. _____

2. _____

3. _____

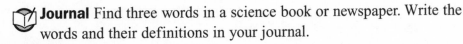 **Journal** Find three words in a science book or newspaper. Write the words and their definitions in your journal.

Name _____

Suffix –ly

>> **A.** Add the *-ly* suffix to each word in parentheses to complete the sentences.

> A **suffix** is a word part that is added to the end of a base word to change the word's meaning or the way that it is used. The suffix *–ly* means *in some way or manner.* For example, the suffix *–ly* is added to the base word *slow* to make *slowly,* which means "in a slow way."

1. Mr. Harwood warned Jordie to perform the

sniff test **(cautious)** _____.

2. Jordie knew **(exact)** _____
what he would do for his science-fair project.

3. After Jordie **(complete)** _____ finished his lab notes, he went to visit his uncle.

4. When they saw Jordie's project, his classmates would **(final)** _____ stop laughing at him.

5. The whole class screamed when the corpse **(sudden)** _____ sat up.

>> **B.** Write your own sentences using the following words with the *-ly* suffix. Circle the base word in each *–ly* word.

> | exactly | finally | cautiously | suddenly |

1. _____

_____

2. _____

_____

3. _____

_____

4. _____

Journal Write three sentences that describe how you feel after reading a scary story. Use a word with the *-ly* suffix in each sentence.

LA.A.1.3.4.7.2 Restates or paraphrases text by summarizing
LA.A.2.3.1.7.1 Extends the expectations of the sixth grade with increasingly complex reading texts and assignments and tasks

Name _____

Summarize

>> **A.** Reread Scene 6 of "Jordie's Revenge." Fill in the graphic organizer with key events and information from the scene. The first one is done for you.

> A **summary** contains the most important details or events in a text.

1. Important Detail or Event Mr. Harwood calls on Jordie.	**2. Important Detail or Event**
3. Important Detail or Event	**4. Important Detail or Event**
5. Important Detail or Event	**6. Important Detail or Event**

>> **B.** Now write a summary of Scene 6 using the key events and information from the boxes above.

_____

_____

_____

_____

_____

Name _____

Idioms

>> A. Read each sentence below. Underline the idiom. The first one is done for you.

> An **idiom** is a phrase or expression that means something different from what the words actually say. For instance, when Norm says, "*Business is dead,*" he means that business is slow.

1. Upset about science class, Jordie walked into Norm's business looking like <u>something the cat dragged in.</u>

2. Norm convinced Jordie to spill his secret.

3. Mr. Harwood wondered whether Jordie had the stomach for handling a corpse.

4. Jordie was so excited he could hardly stand it.

5. Norm was late because he got hung up at work.

>> B. Draw a line to connect each idiom with its meaning.

Idioms	Meanings
1. could hardly stand	was able to tolerate
2. spill	was delayed
3. had the stomach for	messy; stressed out
4. got hung up	tell
5. something the cat dragged in	was almost overcome by

○ **Activity** Tell a partner a story about something scary that happened to you. In your story, use two or three of the idioms from this lesson.

Writing & Grammar

LA.D.1.3.1.7.1 Identifies patterns and rules found in the English language

Name _____

Action Verbs With Direct Objects

> **A.** Underline the action verb in each sentence. Then circle the direct object. The first one is done for you.

> An **action verb** is a word that shows action. A **direct object** is a noun or pronoun that follows an action verb. It receives the action of the verb. For example, in the sentence, "*The dog munched the bone,*" *munched* is the verb and *bone* is the direct object that receives the action: *munched*.

1. Jordie sniffed the (compound) in the test tube.
2. Mr. Harwood scolded Jordie for his sloppy lab work.
3. Jordie dropped the test tube on the floor..
4. Marvin wheeled the casket into the classroom.
5. The corpse chased the students out the door.

> **B.** Write three sentences. In each sentence, use one action verb and one direct object from the word bank.

Word Bank	
action verbs	**direct objects**
shock	students
scare	teacher
inspect	test tube
switch	places

1. _____
2. _____
3. _____

> **C.** Write a short paragraph about something scary. Underline each action verb you use and circle each direct object.

_____
_____
_____

Name _____

Plan a Schedule

>> Look again at the weekly schedule on page 112 of your book as you complete this activity.

Use your list from "Make a List" on page 113 of your book. Use the schedule below to organize your activities. First write in the things you have to do. Then use the remaining time to schedule the things you do for fun.

> Use arrows to show how long your activities last.

	Monday	Tuesday	Wednesday	Thursday	Friday
6 A.M.					
7 A.M.					
8 A.M.					
9 A.M.					
10 A.M.					
11 A.M.					
12 NOON					
1 P.M.					
2 P.M.					
3 P.M.					
4 P.M.					
5 P.M.					
6 P.M.					
7 P.M.					
8 P.M.					
9 P.M.					
10 P.M.					
11 P.M.					
12 MIDNIGHT					

LA.A.1.3.2.7.2 Uses context clues to interpret the meaning of what is read

Name _____

Words, Words, Words

exhausted: very tired
disobey: to go against the rules or someone's wishes
signature: your full name written in script
gazed: looked at something for a long time
settled: made one's self comfortable
official: a person in a high position

>> **A.** Fill in each blank with a word from the box.

1. We _____ in amazement at the number of people outside.

2. They can get in trouble if they _____ the government.

3. He was an _____ who worked for the Japanese government.

4. Hundreds of _____ grown-ups waited, their eyes red from lack of sleep.

5. He wrote his _____ on a piece of paper.

6. They all hoped to be _____ in a new home far from the coming war.

>> **B.** Write four sentences of your own. Use one vocabulary word in each sentence.

1. _____

2. _____

3. _____

4. _____

Journal Find three words in the newspaper about people who need help. Write them in your journal. Use each word in a sentence.

Passage to Freedom

Name _____

Inflectional Endings

>> **A.** Add the ending to each word below. Change the the spelling, if neccessary.

> The **inflectional endings** -ed and -ing can be added to an action word to change the time of the action. When you add -ed or -ing to a word that ends in e, drop the e (change, changed, changing). When you add -ed to a word that ends in consonant -y, change the y to i (fry, fried).

  1. chase + -ing _____

  2. hop + -ed _____

  3. spy + -ed _____

  4. jump + -ed _____

  5. race + -ing _____

>> **B.** Fill in the blanks in each sentence below with the word shown in parentheses.

  1. The boy did not have enough money for what he _____. (**want + -ed**)

  2. They _____ a cable from Japan. (**receive + -ed**)

  3. Many families needed help _____ the Nazis. (**escape + -ing**)

  4. His father _____ his mind many times. (**change + -ed**)

  5. Children outside the fence were _____. (**cry + -ing**)

>> **C.** Write your own sentences using the base word and ending shown in parentheses.

  1. (cry + -ed) _____

  2. (write + -ing) _____

  3. (come + -ing) _____

Journal Find three words in a magazine that contain a base word plus an ending. Record them and the base words in your journal.

Name _____

Make Inferences

>> **A.** Complete the chart below with clues from
   the text and your own inferences.

> An **inference** is a reasonable
> guess based on text clues and
> your own knowledge and
> experience.

WHAT I LEARNED FROM READING	WHAT I ALREADY KNOW
Even though the Japanese government told Mr. Sugihara no, he wrote visas for as many refugees as he could.	People who do what they know is right are

MY INFERENCE

Mr. Sugihara

>> **B.** Reread page 117. Make an inference about why Mr. Sugihara invites only five
   refugees into his house to talk. Draw your own Make Inferences chart to record
   your work.

WHAT I LEARNED FROM READING: Mr. Sugihara invites five men into his
house to talk.

WHAT I ALREADY KNOW: _____

MY INFERENCE: _____

Passage to Freedom

Name _____

Word Order

>> **A.** Draw a line to separate the subject from the predicate. Circle the verb in the predicate. The first one is done for you.

1. My father (peered) through the curtains at the crowd.
2. The diplomat met with five men.
3. Hundreds of Jewish refugees waited outside the house.
4. The crowd wanted visas.

> **Word order** is the arrangement of words in a sentence. In English, most sentences begin with the subject followed by the predicate. The subject tells who or what the sentence is about. The predicate tells what the subject is or does. The predicate is made up of the verb and sometimes an object.
> Example:
>
> subject   predicate
> Many people / ate the food.
>   verb

>> **B.** Rewrite the sentences using correct word order. Write each sentence on the line.

1. orders government disobeyed He.

   _____

2. wanted They visas exit.

   _____

3. cable We to Japan sent a.

   _____

4. followed train They the.

   _____

5. helped family My hundreds people of.

   _____

⬡ **Activity** Tell a partner about someone you admire. Then switch roles.

Name _____

Compound Sentences

> A compound sentence is a sentence made up of two simple sentences joined by a comma and the word *or, and,* or *but*.

>> **A.** Read each compound sentence. Circle the joining word and underline the two simple sentences it joins. The first sentence has been done for you.

1. Mr. Sugihara could obey his government, (or) he could listen to his conscience.

2. He chose to follow his conscience, and he stayed up for many nights.

3. The refugees were grateful for his efforts, but they were sad at the same time.

4. The Sugiharas left, and the Lithuanians never saw their "hero" again.

5. You have a hero inside, but you must look for it.

>> **B.** Rewrite the simple sentences below to make compound sentences. Use the joining word in parentheses ( ).

1. The day was warm. The refugees wore winter coats. **(but)**

_____

2. They waited in front of the house. They waited in the garage. **(and)**

_____

3. The children held onto their mothers. They clung to their fathers. **(or)**

_____

4. My father walked outside. I peered through the curtains. **(and)**

_____

>> **C.** Complete each compound sentence by adding another simple sentence.

1. After school I will do my homework, and _____.

2. The football game was exciting, but _____.

3. We can go to a movie, or _____.

Name _____

Editor for a Day

>> Look again at the newspaper index on page 126 of your book as you complete this activity.

> Use the sample index on page 126 of your book to look up the letter of each section of *The Daily News*.

You are the editor of *The Daily News*. Using the chart below, create an index listing the section and page for these stories: "Montreal Canadiens to Make Stanley Cup Play-Offs," "Another Bad Day for U.S. Stocks," "President to Visit Kenya," and "Mayor Wins Re-election in Close Race."

The Daily News

Story	Section	Page

Name _____

Words, Words, Words

> **frustrated:** helpless or discouraged
> **clutching:** holding on tightly
> **tragedy:** a very sad event
> **anxious:** worried
> **hazard:** a danger or a risk
> **muffler:** something that reduces the noise made by a car engine

➤➤ A. Can you find the missing words? Fill in each blank with a word from the box.

1. Mr. Candler could tell from the _____ look on the student's face that she was helpless and discouraged.

2. She was tightly _____ a handkerchief as she spoke.

3. After she lost her jewelry, she became worried and looked _____.

4. He described the _____ of the plane crash that led to living with his uncle.

5. On the way to school, the _____ fell off Mr. Candler's car.

6. Grease fires can be a _____ in a snack bar kitchen.

➤➤ B. Write three sentences of your own about teenage problems. Use a word from the box in each sentence.

1. _____

2. _____

3. _____

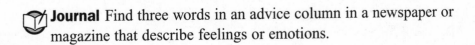 **Journal** Find three words in an advice column in a newspaper or magazine that describe feelings or emotions.

Mr. Candler

Name _____

Contractions

A **contraction** is a short form of two words. An apostrophe takes the place of the missing letter or letters.
Example: *did not = didn't*

Contractions with:

not	is	are	had	have
didn't	he's	they're	they'd	I've
isn't	it's	we're	he'd	they've

>> **A.** Circle the contraction. On the line, write the two words that form the contraction.

1. They'd seen Mr. Candler at school.   _____

2. I've lost my necklace.   _____

3. He's hurt by the linebacker.   _____

4. This isn't a good day for Virginia.   _____

5. They're all good students, he thought.   _____

>> **B.** Complete each sentence with one of the words from the box.

1. _____ a necklace her grandfather gave to her.

2 The girls have met and _____ both promised not to fight.

3. _____ all going to the movies, aren't we?

4. I'm sure he _____ talk to anyone yesterday.

5. He said _____ keep his promise, and I believe him.

Journal Find three contractions in a magazine. Write the contractions and the words they stand for in your journal.

Mr. Candler

LA.A.1.3.4.7.3 Uses a graphic organizer to clarify the meaning of text
LA.A.2.3.1.7.1 Extends the expectations of the sixth grade with increasingly complex reading
texts and assignments and tasks

Name _____

Analyze Character

>> **A.** Complete the character chart for Mr. Candler.
Fill in the missing information.

A **character** is a person written about in a story. You can learn about characters by paying attention to what they do, what they say, what they think, and what others say about them— or how others act towards them.

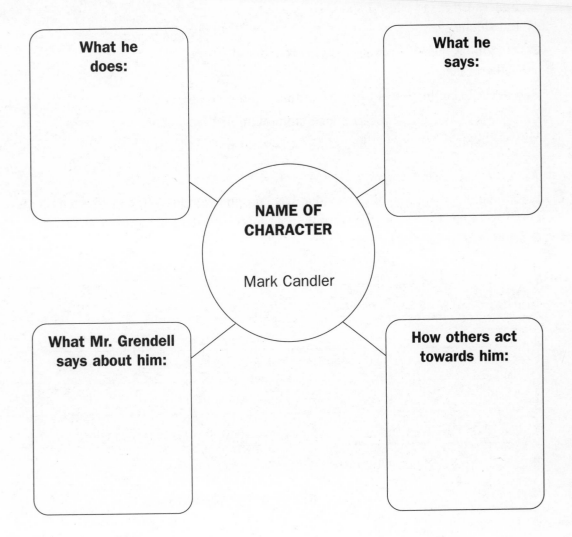

What he does:

What he says:

NAME OF CHARACTER

Mark Candler

What Mr. Grendell says about him:

How others act towards him:

>> **B.** Select another character in the story. Make your own character chart on another piece of paper.

Mr. Candler

Name _____

Informal Language

>> **A.** The sentences below might be spoken by one of
the characters from "My Friend's Got This Problem,
Mr. Candler." Each contains one or more words
with dropped letters. Add apostrophes to
show where letters have been dropped.

> Sometimes writers drop letters
> from words spoken by
> characters to capture the
> sound of **informal language**
> used in speech. Dropped letters
> are always shown by an
> apostrophe (').
> Here are a few examples:
> *working* ⇨ *workin'*
> *acting* ⇨ *actin'*
> *about* ⇨ *'bout*

1. I guess I feel sad cause I spend so much
   time alone.

2. My kid brother was always hangin around and
   botherin me.

3. I never liked the things I heard Virginia sayin bout me.

4. I guess I can wait til you get done talkin with that student.

5. Whose business is it if I like sendin Lizette Ramirez hearts?

>> **B.** Find three other words in the story that have dropped letters. Write each word on the
numbered line. Then write the word without missing letters. Finally use the word
in a sentence.

1. _____   _____   _____

   _____

2. _____   _____   _____

   _____

3. _____   _____   _____

   _____

○ **Activity** Describe something that happened in school yesterday in one sentence. Use
at least one word with a dropped letter. Have a partner write down exactly what you
say. Circle the word or words with dropped letters. Then switch roles.

LA.D.1.3.1.7.1 Identifies patterns and rules found in the English language

Name _____

Quotation Marks for Dialogue

> When writing dialogue, or a conversation, use **quotation marks** (" ") to show the exact words of each speaker. Begin quotations with capital letters. Separate the quotation from the words after it with a comma or other punctuation. Begin a new paragraph for each speaker.

>> A. Read the sentences. Add the missing quotation marks in each sentence.

1. Mr. Candler? asked the voice on the telephone.

2. You don't know me, sir, but I know all about you, he said.

3. She asked, Where are you going, Mr. Candler?

4. My aunt and uncle are good to me, he said, but they will never take the place of my parents.

5. Lizette said, Who keeps putting those hearts on my desk?

>> B. Read the sentences. Add the missing commas and quotation marks.

1. Mother asked Did you do your homework, Amelia?

2. I will just as soon as Amy gets off the computer Amelia answered.

3. Then Amy said When I finish my e-mail, you can have the computer.

4. Did I get any e-mail Amy asked her sister.

5. Yes! said Amelia. There's a message from you-know-who!

>> C. What would you like to ask Mr. Candler? Write a short conversation you might have with him. Use quotation marks. Remember to begin a new paragraph each time the speaker changes.

_____

_____

_____

_____

_____

LA.A.2.3.5.7.2 Compiles, organizes, and interprets information for a variety of purposes

Name _____

Phone Tag

>> Look again at the business message on page 140 of your book as you complete this activity.

If the caller leaves a fax or cell phone number, check the correct box. Also, be sure to write neatly.

Bailey Flynn just returned Goldie Silver's call. Her assistant, Beth Scott, answered and said Ms. Silver was out to lunch. Bailey left his cell phone number so that Goldie could reach him anytime. On the business message form below, create the message that Beth took.

Phone Call		
For _____ Date _____ Time _____ AM/PM		
M _____		
Of _____		
Phone ☐ Fax ☐ Cell _____		
Area Code Number Extension		
Message _____		Phoned
_____		Returned Your Call
_____		Please Call
_____		Will Call Again
Signed _____		Came to See You
		Wants to See You

Mr. Candler

Name _____

Words, Words, Words

> **consisted:** made up of
>
> **equivalent:** equal in value
>
> **distinctive:** clearly different
>
> **penalized:** punished for something done wrong
>
> **guaranteed:** certain that something will happen
>
> **representative:** a person or thing that is typical of a group

>> A. Can you find the missing word? Fill in each blank with a word from the box.

1. Her Earth family _____ of her mother and herself.

2. Someone thought she was _____ of typical Earth kids.

3. Would she be _____ for having only two arms and two eyes?

4. Each Zyglotian had a _____ third eye, which made them look very different from Earthlings.

5. In the Zyglot language "Em" was the _____ of "Mom."

6. Getting used to living on another world was _____ to be difficult.

>> B. Write three original sentences. Use one vocabulary word in each.

1. _____

2. _____

3. _____

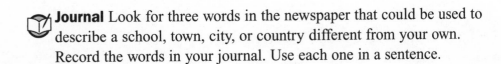 **Journal** Look for three words in the newspaper that could be used to describe a school, town, city, or country different from your own. Record the words in your journal. Use each one in a sentence.

LA.D.1.3.1.7.1 Identifies patterns and rules found in the English language

Name _____

Possessives

>> **A.** Underline the word in each sentence with an apostrophe. Decide if it is a singular possessive noun or a plural possesive noun. Circle singular or plural.

> **Possessives** show ownership. To form the possessive of a singular noun, add an apostrophe and s. To show ownership of a plural noun, add s' to the end of the word. Example: The bird's wing (singular). The birds' wings (plural).

1. Earth's inhabitants have only two arms and two eyes.   singular   plural

2. Students at the school made fun of the narrator's two blue eyes.   singular   plural

3. The girls' room had sinks and stalls, just like on Earth.   singular   plural

4. Zyglotians' eyes were each a different color.   singular   plural

5. Before attempting to play boodlach, you may want to learn the game's rules.   singular   plural

6. Grudnick's secret was that all three of her eyes were the same color.   singular   plural

>> **B.** Write sentences of your own for each possessive noun in parentheses ( ).

1. (year's) _____.

2. (mother's) _____.

3. (boys') _____.

4. (stars') _____.

Journal Look for three possessive nouns in a magazine. Record them in your journal. Use each one in a sentence.

Name _____

Analyze Setting

▶▶ Complete the chart below by adding more information about the setting of "Young Blue Eyes." Fill in the empty boxes.

> The **setting** is the time and place of a story. The setting can affect things a character does. It can also affect what happens in the story.

Place	Time
	The story takes place in the future when people from Earth are able to travel to and live on other planets.

Details About the Setting	How the Setting Affects Character and Events
• Doorknobs are in the middle of the doors.	• The narrator finds herself bumping into doors.
• The Zyglots have three arms.	• The narrator, who has two arms, made a fool of herself trying to play a game requiring the use of the third arm.
• The Zyglots have three eyes, each with a different color.	• The narrator cries when classmates make fun of her eyes.
•	•
•	•

Young Blue Eyes

Name _____

Idioms

An **idiom** is a phrase which means something different from what the words actually say. For example, *a fish out of water* means "to feel uncomfortable or out of place."

>> **A.** Read each sentence below. Circle the idiom.

1. To kids from Earth, Zyglot kids were their worst nightmare.
2. She promised she'd stay in touch with her Earth friends.
3. The narrator and Grudnick always had a blast when they were together.
4. They'd been shoveling Zyglotian history down her throat for months.
5. The history teacher got a kick out of her knowing important Zyglotian dates and leaders.

>> **B.** Match the idiom on the left with its meaning on the right.

1. no big deal   a. the way things turned out
2. feel at home   b. spend time with
3. hang out with   c. stay nearby
4. ended up   d. not very important
5. stick around   e. to feel comfortable

>> **C.** Write three sentences of your own using three idioms from above.

1. _____

_____

2. _____

_____

3. _____

_____

⭕ **Activity** Have a conversation with a partner about a school activity. Use at least two idioms in your speech.

Name _____

Possessive Nouns

> **A.** Complete each sentence with a possessive. Use one of the words in parentheses.

> A **possessive noun** is a person, place, or thing that shows ownership. Singular possessive nouns usually end in 's. Plural nouns that end in s show possession by adding an apostrophe after the s.

   1. The _____ gravitational pull made it difficult for the spaceship to blast off. **(planet's, planets')**

   2. The _____ performance was disappointing. **(team's, teams')**

   3. The _____ locker room is down the hall. **(girl's, girls')**

   4. It is through the door past the _____ lounge. **(teacher's, teachers')**

> **B.** Rewrite each item with a possessive noun.

   1. The car of the coach was parked on the street.

   _____

   2. The store belonging to her two uncles is next to the library.

   _____

   3. The puppies of his pet beagle are cute.

   _____

   4. Have you seen the case that belongs to this video?

   _____

> **C.** Make each noun into a possessive. Use the possessive form in a sentence of your own.

   1. visitor: _____

   2. family: _____

Name _____

Find It Fast

>> Look again at the home page on page 154 of your book as you complete this activity.

Here are a few things you might want to find on the Web. List the words and phrases you would use to search for each one.

> Before you use a search engine, click the "Help" button. Then print out the tips for conducting a good search.

1. A Web site that sells CDs _____

_____

_____

_____

2. Career home-run leaders in major league baseball _____

_____

_____

_____

3. A group devoted to fighting drug abuse in schools _____

_____

_____

_____

4. Help with your math homework _____

_____

_____

_____

5. Places to go skateboarding in San Francisco _____

_____

_____

_____

Young Blue Eyes

Name _____

Words, Words, Words

> **influence:** have an effect upon; affect; change
> **scent:** a pleasant smell
> **tempted:** to want something or want to do something; attracted
> **display:** show
> **impulse:** a sudden desire to do something
> **advertisers:** people who give information about products for sale

>> A. Can you find the missing words? Fill in each blank with a word from the box.

Catchy descriptions of products are written by (1) _____. Stores

(2) _____ the products in an attractive way. They will try to

(3) _____ shoppers any way they can by affecting shoppers' senses.

The sweet (4) _____ of a new perfume or the aroma of baked cookies

will hopefully lure shoppers into the store. The longer people stay in a store, the

more (5) _____ they will be to buy something. Retailers place small

goodies next to the cash register, hoping you will buy one last item on

(6) _____ .

>> B. Describe an ad that would influence you to buy the product. Use one or more
vocabulary words in your description.

_____

_____

_____

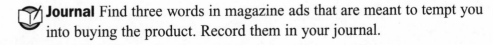 **Journal** Find three words in magazine ads that are meant to tempt you
into buying the product. Record them in your journal.

Don't Be Fooled

Name _____

Homophones

➤➤ **A.** Read each sentence below. Circle the homophone that fits in each sentence and then write it on the line.

> **Homophones** are words that sound alike but have different spellings and meanings. (Example: *hear/here*)

1. Do you ever _____ things that you do not need? **(buy, by)**

2. The _____ of the perfume filled the air. **(sent, scent)**

3. Which pair of shoes will you _____ today? **(where, wear)**

4. Cosmetics are in the center _____ of the store. **(I'll, aisle)**

5. Most people turn to the _____ when they enter a store. **(write, right)**

6. He bought _____ sweaters on sale. **(for, four)**

➤➤ **B.** Write a sentence for each homophone choice above that you did *not* use.

1. _____

2. _____

3. _____

4. _____

5. _____

6. _____

📕 **Journal** Write two more pairs of homophones in your journal. Use each word in a sentence.

Don't Be Fooled

LA.A.1.3.4.7.3 Uses a graphic organizer to clarify the meaning of text
LA.A.2.3.1.7.1 Extends the expectations of the sixth grade with increasingly complex reading texts and assignments and tasks

Name _____

Cause and Effect

>> **A.** Reread "Don't Be Fooled." Then look at the chart below. Read the cause. Then complete each effect.

> A **cause** is an event that makes something happen. To find a cause, ask, *why?*
> An **effect** is what happens. To find an effect, ask, *what happened?*

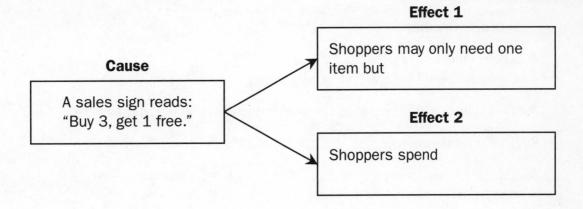

Cause

A sales sign reads: "Buy 3, get 1 free."

Effect 1

Shoppers may only need one item but

Effect 2

Shoppers spend

>> **B.** Read the effect. Fill in a cause.

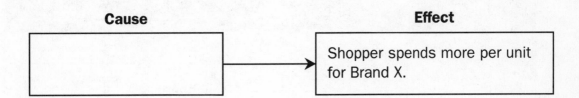

Cause

Effect

Shopper spends more per unit for Brand X.

Name _____

Adjectives That Compare

>> **A.** Complete each sentence with an adjective. Choose one of the words in parentheses ( ).

> **Comparative** adjectives compare two people, things, or ideas. Most comparative adjectives are formed by adding -er or using the word *more*.
> **Superlative** adjectives compare three or more people, things, or ideas. Most superlatives are formed by adding -est or using the word *most*.

1. The salesperson said that this stereo is

   _____ than that one.
   (good, better, best)

2. These sunglasses are the _____ expensive ones I've ever had. **(more, most)**

3. This is the _____ model in the store. **(newer, newest)**

4. This price is _____ than the old one. **(lower, lowest)**

5. The first salesperson was _____ helpful than the second. **(more, most)**

>> **B.** Read the chart. Fill in the missing comparative or superlative adjective.

Adjective	Comparative	Superlative
1. loud	louder	_____
2. cheap	_____	cheapest
3. fast	faster	_____
4. delicious	_____	most delicious
5. up-to-date	more up-to-date	_____

Activity Describe a favorite place to shop to a partner. Use at least one comparative and one superlative adjective from the chart.

Don't Be Fooled

Name _____

Possessive Pronouns

>> **A.** Underline the possessive pronoun in each sentence.

> **1.** We have a new mall outside our town.
>
> **2.** The toy department has its own floor.
>
> **3.** The experts share their research with store owners.
>
> **4.** His advice led to the remodeling of the mall.
>
> **5.** Those small shops are more interesting than your department store.

> A **possessive pronoun** shows ownership.
> Possessive pronouns that modify nouns are: *my, your, his, her, its, our, their.* (Example: It is *my* dog.)
> Possessive pronouns that can stand alone are: *mine, yours, hers, his, ours, theirs.* (Example: The dog is *mine.*)

>> **B.** Read each sentence. Fill in each blank with a possessive pronoun that can stand alone. Use a form of the word in parentheses. (Hint: Look at the list of possessive pronouns that can stand alone in the gray box.)

> **1.** The store with the sale was _____. (my)
>
> **2.** The idea to play music in the mall was _____. (her)
>
> **3.** The coupons for the sale were _____. (our)
>
> **4.** The colorful advertisement was _____. (their)

>> **C.** Write a sentence using each possessive pronoun in parentheses ( ).

> **1.** (his) _____
>
> **2.** (hers) _____
>
> **3.** (their) _____

Don't Be Fooled

Name _____

Graph-o-Matic

>> Look again on page 164 of your book as you complete this activity.

> Amounts in bar graphs are always measured with bars. Draw bars similar to the ones in the chart on page 164.

Suppose each bar on the graph stands for one person. Show what each of these people's salaries would be if:

- the surgeon's salary drops by $50,000.

- the barber has a new hit salon and his salary triples.

- the detective gets a $20,000 bonus.

Create a graph that shows these three people's new salaries.

SALARIES PER YEAR

$225,000
$200,000
$175,000
$150,000
$125,000
$100,000
$75,000
$50,000
$25,000
$0

Barber   Private Detective   Surgeon

Don't Be Fooled

Name _____

Words, Words, Words

> **relief:** a bringing of comfort or a reduction of pain
>
> **mission:** a special job or task
>
> **overwhelmed:** having too many problems and worries to deal with
>
> **determination:** a strong passion to complete a task despite its difficulty
>
> **indifferent:** not caring or concerned about something
>
> **crisis:** a time of danger and difficulty

>> **A.** Can you find the missing words? Fill in each blank with a word from the box.

When a (1) _____ occurs, many people and organizations

arrive to help out. Volunteers for a (2) _____ organization

try to help others. These people show great (3) _____ to get

the job done. Their (4) _____ is to help others anytime,

anywhere. They are often (5) _____ by so many problems.

These selfless volunteers are never (6) _____, or uncaring, to

the needs of others.

>> **B.** Think of a problem in your school or town. Write five sentences about how the problem might be solved. Use a vocabulary word in each sentence.

1. _____

2. _____

3. _____

4. _____

5. _____

Journal Find three other words in the newspaper that describe heroic characteristics. Write them in your journal.

LA.A.1.3.2.7.1 Uses knowledge of word parts to determine the meaning of unfamiliar words in a literary or informative text

Name _____

Roots

>> **A.** Use the roots in the box to figure out the meaning of the underlined word. Then write the word's meaning in the space provided.

> A **root** is a word or word part from Latin or another language that is used to build English words. One example of a root is *viv*, which means "live." (*survive, revive, vivid*)

> *fug* = flee   *med* = doctor
>
> *viv* = live   *pol* = citizen/people

1. The <u>refugees</u> had to leave their country because of war.

   _____

2. Because of the county's <u>politics</u>, it was dangerous for them to stay.

   _____

3. Many of them were sick and they needed <u>medicine</u>.

   _____

4. They hoped that they could <u>survive</u> until help arrived.

   _____

>> **B.** The root *terra* means "land." Look through the dictionary for two words built on the root *terra*. Write each word and its meaning. Then use each word in a sentence.

1. word: _____   meaning: _____

   _____

2. word: _____   meaning: _____

   _____

🔖 **Journal** Look through magazines or newspapers to find two familiar words with roots you can identify. Write the roots, the words, and the definition of the words in your journal.

Doctors Without Borders

LA.A.1.3.4.7.3 Uses a graphic organizer to clarify the meaning of text
LA.A.2.3.1.7.1 Extends the expectations of the sixth grade with increasingly complex reading texts and assignments and tasks

Name _____

Problem and Solution

>> **A.** Reread page 170. Then use information about how Doctors Without Borders solved the problems.

A **problem** is a challenge or difficulty. The steps toward a solution are the **attempts** taken to solve the problem.
A **solution** is an action that fixes or solves the problem.

PROBLEM
A huge earthquake hits Turkey. Many people are hurt and homeless.

ATTEMPTS

SOLUTION

LA.A.1.3.2.7.1 Uses knowledge of word parts to determine the meaning of unfamiliar words in a literary or informative text

Name _____

Suffixes Indicating Person

> A suffix is a word part added to the end of a word or a base word. The suffixes -or, -er, and -eer mean "a person who."

>> A. Read the words in the box. Then add -or, -er, or -eer to each word to indicate a person and fill in the blanks with the appropriate noun.

| engineer | doctor | volunteer | worker | organizer |

1. The doct_____ rushed to the aid of the refugees.

2. William was trained as an engin_____.

3. The injured work_____ was brought to the hospital.

4. She wasn't afraid to work as a volunt_____ in a dangerous situation.

5. The organiz_____ arranges for medical teams and supplies to be sent.

>> B. Circle the suffix indicating "a person who" in each numbered word below. Then draw a line from the word to its meaning.

1. actor   **a.** one who auctions

2. teacher   **b.** a person who acts

3. creator   **c.** one who designs

4. designer   **d.** a person who teaches

5. auctioneer   **e.** one who makes or creates

⬤ **Activity** Tell a partner about three possible careers that interest you. Use three words with a suffix indicating "a person who."

Doctors Without Borders

Name _____

Proper Nouns

> A **proper noun** names a particular person, place, or thing and begins with a capital letter.

>> A. Underline the letters in the proper nouns that should be capitalized in the sentences below. You can find the nouns on pages 167–168 of your book if you need help.

1. The winner of the nobel peace prize was doctors without borders.

2. Volunteer william conk works at the university of new hampshire.

3. Volunteer christine nadori was sent to sudan.

4. Volunteer stefano sereno is a mexican doctor.

5. He spent months in chechnya after its war with russia.

>> B. Use each proper noun from "Doctors Without Borders" in a sentence of your own.

1. Kenya _____

2. African _____

3. French _____

>> C. On the short line, write a proper noun for each category. Then use the proper noun in a sentence of your own. Write the sentence on the long line.

1. person: _____

_____

2. place: _____

_____

LA.A.2.3.5.7.2 Compiles, organizes, and interprets information for a variety of purposes

Name _____

Check It Out

>> Look again at the airline schedule on page 174 of your book as you complete this activity.

> If you have to change planes, write the connecting flight information for the appropriate player in the second rows.

You're a travel agent. You need to buy tickets for a basketball team traveling from Denver to Washington, D.C. Pick flights for the following players and fill in the schedule below.

- **The two forwards like to sleep late and don't want to change planes.**
- **The two guards like to travel early in the morning.**
- **The center wants to buy souvenirs at the St. Louis airport.**

	Airline	Leave Place/Time	Arrive Place/Time	Nonstop? (yes or no)
Forwards				
Guards				
Center				

Name _____

Words, Words, Words

> **hilarious:** very funny
> **accidentally:** unexpectedly
> **officially:** in a formal way that is approved by authority
> **impressed:** affected strongly, influenced
> **dangling:** swinging or hanging down loosely
> **groaned:** made a harsh sound as if in pain

>> **A.** Complete each sentence with a word from the box.

1. It was so cold that icicles were _____ from the roof.

2. Kenny tripped _____ and fell headfirst into a snowbank.

3. The first blizzard of the season meant winter was _____ here.

4. Byron and Buphead think their pranks are _____.

5. Byron _____, "I think I'm frozen."

6. He yelled for help, but no one seemed _____ by his situation.

>> **B.** Think about what happened to Byron. Now think of a strange or weird event that you know about. Write four sentences about the event using a vocabulary word in each sentence.

1. _____

2. _____

3. _____

4. _____

Journal Find three words about winter or cold in the selection. Write them in your journal.

Name _____

Homophones

>> **A.** Draw a line from each homophone to its meaning.

1. right	to put words on paper	
write	correct	
2. two	a number	
too	also	
3. due	expected at a certain time	
do	to perform an action	
4. knew	not used	
new	had knowledge of	
5. their	they are	
there	belonging to them	
they're	that place	

>> **B.** Complete the sentences using words from the box.

1. They wore _____ heaviest clothes when they scraped the ice.

2. They were _____ at Aunt Cydney's for a visit very soon.

3. Byron didn't always do the _____ thing.

4. Kenny _____ better, but he trusted his mean older brother anyway.

5. Kenny had on _____ pairs of mittens and three pairs of pants.

Journal Look for homophones as you read a magazine or newspaper. Write several pairs of homophones in your journal along with their meanings. Use a dictionary for help.

LA.A.1.3.4.7.3 Uses a graphic organizer to clarify the meaning of text
LA.A.2.3.1.7.1 Extends the expectations of the sixth grade with increasingly complex reading texts and assignments and tasks

Name _____

Cause and Effect

>> Reread the section of the story on pages 180–181. Look at the chart. When you're given the cause, write the effect. When you're given the effect, write the cause. Remember that the effect of one thing may become the cause of something else.

> A **cause** is an event that makes something happen. An **effect** is what happens as a result of something else.

Cause:	Effect:
	Byron bangs on the car door.

Cause:	Effect:
Byron bangs on the car door.	

Cause:	Effect:
Kenny tells his parents Byron is crying.	

Meet the Weird Watsons

Name _____

Slang

>> **A.** Read each sentence. Circle the letter next to the word or phrase that has the same meaning as the underlined slang expression in the sentence.

> **Standard English** is the form of English you use for school and work. **Slang** is more informal. It is used mostly in conversation rather than in writing.

1. Byron called Kenny a " square ."

    a. a thin person   **b.** an old-fashioned person

2. Did you see my baby bruh headfirst in the snowbank?

    a. younger brother   **b.** small brush

3. By went nuts when Dad pulled his ear.

    a. acted hungry   **b.** acted upset

4. The dirty dogs let Byron get away with everything.

    a. unfair people   **b.** unclean animals

5. Dad called Byron a "knucklehead ."

    a. someone who cracks knuckles   **b.** someone who is not smart

>> **B.** Each sentence below contains a slang expression. Rewrite each sentence so that it expresses the same idea in standard English.

1. "No one's as cool as I am," thought Byron.

_____

2. Byron was not usually a cry baby.

_____

3. Kenny flunked the blizzard test.

_____

○ **Activity** Brainstorm with a partner two or more slang expressions. Have a conversation with each other using the examples of slang.

Name _____

Verb Tenses

>> **A.** Complete the box by filling in the missing verb tenses.

A verb in the **present tense** shows action that happens now. A verb in the **past tense** shows action that has already happened. A verb in the **future tense** shows action that will happen in the future.

Present	Past	Future
1. tell	told	
2.	gave	will give
3. hear		will hear
4.	stuck	
5.	laughed	

>> **B.** Read each sentence and underline the verb. Identify the verb's tense and write it on the line: *present*, *past*, or *future*. The first one is done for you.

1. Kenny will tell many stories about his hero, the Lipless Wonder. ___future___

2. Buphead gives Kenny a mean test. _____

3. Kenny heard his big brother Byron. _____

4. Byron's lips stuck to the mirror. _____

5. You will laugh at this story, too! _____

>> **C.** Write three sentences about a family. Use the verb tense shown in parentheses ( ).

1. (present) _____

2. (past) _____

3. (future) _____

LA.A.2.3.5.7.2 Compiles, organizes, and interprets information for a variety of purposes

Name _____

Solve the Problem

>> Look again at the road signs on page 188 of your book as you complete this activity.

Review your list of three driving mistakes from "Watch the Road" on page 189. Design a sign that would help solve each problem. Use what you learned about road signs in this lesson. Record your ideas in the chart below.

> Try to use appropriate shapes and symbols when designing your signs.

Driving Mistake	Design a Sign

Helpful Hint: You may wish to design signs for the following: no right turn; slow down, speed limit is 25; stop when you come to a crosswalk.

Name _____

Words, Words, Words

> **mortified:** embarrassed enough to feel one's pride is hurt
> **residence:** a place where someone lives
> **acquainted:** having been brought into social contact
> **coping:** dealing with something successfully
> **systematic:** having a method or a plan
> **emigrated:** moved from one country to another

>> A. Can you find the missing words? Fill in each blank with a word from the box.

The Lin family (1) _____ from China to America. Their new

(2) _____ was a house on a tree-lined street. They become happily (3)

_____ with their neighbors, the Gleason family. There were so many

new things to get used to, the Lins had trouble (4) _____. At the

Gleasons' dinner party the Lins were (5) _____ after bringing chairs to

the table and discovering it was a buffet dinner! One way Mr. Lin handled things was

by developing a logical and (6) _____ approach to learning English.

>> B. Write four sentences about meeting someone or doing something for the first time.
Use one vocabulary word in each sentence.

1. _____

2. _____

3. _____

4. _____

Journal Find three words in a magazine about food. Write them in
your journal.

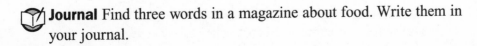

The All-American Slurp

LA.D.2.3.2.7.1 Uses figurative language techniques

Name _____

Synonyms

> A synonym is a word that has the same or similar meaning as another word.

>> **A.** Read each sentence. On the line, write a word from the box that is a synonym for the underlined word.

> pleasantly   chewing   clean
>
> goods   cautiously

1. To <u>disinfect</u> the raw vegetables, we boiled them. _____

2. The pile of fruit was <u>carefully</u> arranged so that it would not fall.

_____

3. The Lins sat on the couch and appeared to smile <u>happily</u>. _____

4. They watched others <u>munching</u> the raw celery. _____

5. Many <u>products</u> in American stores are not for sale in China. _____

>> **B.** Read each word. Then write two synonyms for each word.

Word	Synonyms
tremendous	_____
glanced	_____
awful	_____

 Journal Choose three verbs from the selection. Then, write several synonyms for each word in your journal. Use a dictionary or thesaurus for help.

The All–American Slurp

LA.A.1.3.4.7.3 Uses a graphic organizer to clarify the meaning of text
LA.A.2.3.1.7.1 Extends the expectations of the sixth grade with increasingly complex reading texts and assignments and tasks

Name _____

Read for Detail

▶▶ **A.** Look at pages 195–196 of the story to read about the Lins' dinner party. Write down important details in the boxes below.

> **Details** are facts or bits of information about a topic that tell *who*, *what*, *where*, *when*, *how*, and *why*. Paying attention to details can help you better understand what you read.

Topic: The Gleasons attend a dinner party at the Lins'.

DETAIL

DETAIL

DETAIL

DETAIL

The All–American Slurp

Name _____

Words That Describe Eating

> A verb is a word that expresses an action or state of being. Some verbs describe eating. Writers use different verbs about eating to express their specific ideas.

>> **A.** Complete each sentence by circling the word that describes eating.

1. The Lins enjoyed the _____ of fresh celery.

crash   crunch   crease

2. Meg _____ her milkshakes when she drinks through a straw.

spills   makes   slurps

3. To try new food, _____ on a bit of it first.

shovel   nibble   wheel

4. The guests had to _____ on the tough meat for a long time.

chew   look   pried

5. The boy filled his mouth and _____ the food quietly.

lifted   swallowed   examined

>> **B.** Choose four of the words you used to complete sentences above. For each word, write a sentence that tells about eating.

1. _____

2. _____

3. _____

4. _____

⬤ **Activity** With a partner, brainstorm a list of words that describe eating. Then tell your partner about your favorite meal, using two or three words from the list.

The All–American Slurp

Name _____

Adjectives

>> **A.** Underline the adjective or adjectives in each sentence. The first one has been done for you.

1. Mrs. Lin cooked a <u>delicious</u> meal.

2. The Gleasons invited the Lins to a special dinner.

3. For dessert, Mrs. Lin served ripe strawberries.

4. There were fifty hungry diners in the restaurant.

5. The Lins ate the hot soup.

6. For a tasty snack, we ate the cold chicken.

> An **adjective** is a word that modifies, or describes, a noun or pronoun. It may appear before or after the word it modifies.
> Examples:
> The <u>creamy</u> milkshake tastes good.
> Meg likes her milkshakes <u>thick</u>.

>> **B.** Complete each sentence by writing an adjective in the blank.

1. Before lunch, we went for a _____ walk.

2. As we walked, we noticed _____ birds overhead.

3. The snow that fell yesterday was _____.

>> **C.** Write three sentences describing a special place. Use at least one adjective in each sentence.

1. _____

2. _____

3. _____

Name _____

Open for Business

>> Look again at the menu on page 200 of your book as you complete this activity.

You're opening a restaurant. What dishes will you serve? Create a menu in the space below.

When you're creating your menu, remember to include appetizers, entrees, desserts, and beverages. Don't forget the prices.

LA.A.1.3.2.7.2 Uses context clues to interpret the meaning of what is read

Name _____

Words, Words, Words

> **strong:** having the power to cause deep feelings
>
> **raggedy:** torn and worn out
>
> **nonsense:** silly or annoying behavior
>
> **grins:** cheerfully smiles
>
> **rattling:** moving noisily
>
> **ache:** to feel pain

>> A. Use one of the words from the box to fill in each blank.

1. No one in the class wants to admit to owning the old and _____ sweater.

2. Sylvia Saldívar, who doesn't like Rachel, reports that the sweater belongs to Rachel and then _____ about the trick.

3. Rachel tries to protest, but the teacher says, "I won't put up with such _____," and places the sweater on Rachel's desk.

4. The teacher's _____ words make Rachel feel bad.

5. Having an unpleasant experience causes Rachel's heart to _____.

6. Rachel feels her nerves _____ like pennies inside her body.

>> B. Write two original sentences about one of the stories by Sandra Cisneros. Use the words shown.

1. nonsense: _____

   _____

2. ache: _____

   _____

Journal Look for three other words in your selection that might be used in a discussion of feelings and experiences that arise during childhood.

Sandra Cisneros: Storyteller

LA.D.2.3.2.7.1 Uses figurative language techniques

Name _____

Connotation and Denotation

> A word's **denotation** is its literal, or dictionary, meaning. **Connotation** refers to the feeling that is brought out by the word.

>> A. Decide whether each underlined word has a positive (good) or negative (bad) connotation. Write a *p* for *positive* or an *n* for *negative* on each line.

1. My great-grandmother was a <u>stubborn</u> woman. _____

2. In Spanish, my name is <u>soft</u>, like silver. _____

3. I <u>shove</u> the sweater to the edge of my desk. _____

4. "Stop that!" <u>scolds</u> Mrs. Price. _____

5. Mrs. Price is usually a <u>fair</u> person. _____

6. We ride the bike past my red, <u>crumbly</u> house. _____

7. Down Mango Street we go, laughing as though we heard a <u>funny</u> joke. _____

8. We have a <u>good</u> time with our new friends. _____

>> B. Choose any three sentences from Part A, and rewrite them using a word with a connotation opposite from the one used.

1. _____

_____

2. _____

_____

3. _____

_____

 Journal Look for three other words in the stories that have either a positive or negative connotation. Write them and their connotations in your journal.

Sandra Cisneros: Storyteller

Comprehension

 LA.A.2.3.1.7.1 Extends the expectations of the sixth grade with increasingly complex reading texts and assignments and tasks

Name _____

Make Inferences

>> **A.** Complete the charts by making inferences about the stories.

> An **inference** is a reasonable guess based on text clues as well as your own knowledge and experience.

1.

What I Learned from Reading	What I Already Know
The great-grandmother in "My Name" was a "horse woman"— born in the Chinese year of the horse.	Horses are strong animals, capable of pulling heavy wagons and doing other chores that require great strength.

My Inference

2.

What I Learned from Reading	What I Already Know
In "Our Good Day," Lucy and Rachel do not laugh, like other children, when they hear Esperanza's name.	

My Inference

Sandra Cisneros: Storyteller

LA.D.1.3.1.7.1 Identifies patterns and rules found in the English language

Name _____

Time Words

>> **A.** Underline the time words in the sentences below.

> **Time words** decribe when an action takes place. They help readers understand the order of events in a story.

    1. Today I had a bad day at school.

    2. I felt sad after Mrs. Price put a raggedy old sweater on my desk.

    3. Before Mrs. Price gave me the ugly sweater, she looked right at me.

    4. Finally, Phyllis remembered that the sweater was hers.

    5. All of a sudden, I was very angry with Phyllis.

>> **B.** Write three original sentences about the characters in the short stories. Use a time word in each sentence.

    1. _____

    _____

    2. _____

    _____

    3. _____

    _____

Activity Tell the class what you are going to do after class today. Use three time words in your description.

Name _____

Subject/Object Pronouns

Personal Pronouns	
Subject	**Object**
I	me
he	him
she	her
they	them
we	us

Personal pronouns take the place of nouns that name people. They have different forms depending on whether they are the **subject** (doer of the action in a sentence) or **object** (receiver of the action).

>> **A.** Fill in the blank with the correct pronoun form.

1. I like to tell stories after the mailman gives _____ the mail. **(I, me)**

2. _____ didn't always live on Mango Street. **(We, Us)**

3. One day our neighbors will notice we are gone, and _____ will say, "What happened to Esperanza?" **(they, them)**

4. I see my Papa cry and don't know what to do for _____. **(he, him)**

5. Because _____ am the oldest, my father has told me to tell the others. **(I, me)**

6. But I like them, especially the big one, who lets the little one talk for

_____. **(she, her)**

>> **B.** Write two original sentences about characters in the short story collection. Each sentence should contain a pronoun from the box at the top of this page.

1. _____

_____

2. _____

_____

Sandra Cisneros: Storyteller

LA.A.2.3.5.7.2 Compiles, organizes, and interprets information for a variety of purposes

Name _____

Total It Up

Keep in mind the amount of each item that you really need.

>> Look again at the label and chart on page 210 of your book as you complete this activity.

It's time to throw a party. You'll use 50 napkins, 14 ounces of salsa, and 3 liters of cola. You want to spend as little as possible. Which brands should you buy? Use the chart below to figure out how much money you will spend.

	Napkins	Salsa	Cola
Brand			
Price			
Quantity			
Total Price			

Sandra Cisneros: Storyteller

Name _____

Words, Words, Words

> **identified:** considered as the same
> **authority:** a high position of power
> **regret:** to be sad or sorry about something
> **humorous:** funny
> **appreciate:** enjoy or value something
> **goals:** things you want to accomplish or achieve

>> **A.** Can you find the missing words? Fill in each blank with a word from the box.

1. Cassandra felt the same as the Judy Blume character. Cassandra

   _____ with her.

2. Cassandra continued to write, even when a teacher, someone in

   _____, discouraged her.

3. People often _____ the bad things they do to others.

4. Many of the kids enjoyed teasing. They thought it was _____.

5. A writer's _____ can be achieved by writing every day.

6. Cassandra's readers _____ her stories of wisdom and motivation.

>> **B.** If you could ask Cassandra Walker three questions, what would they be? Write three questions. Use one vocabulary word in each sentence.

1. _____

2. _____

3. _____

Journal Find three words in the selection that describe things that are unique. Write them in your journal.

LA.D.2.3.2.7.1 Uses figurative language techniques

Antonyms

Name _____

>> **A.** Read the sentences below. Choose an antonym for each word in boldface.

> An **antonym** is a word that means the opposite or nearly the opposite of another word.

1. Cassandra Walker heard all her life that she was too **skinny**.

   a. fat   **b.** thin   **c.** attractive

2. People told her that she was too **ugly**.

   a. unattractive   **b.** popular   **c.** pretty

3. She wrote two books for kids that were big **successes**.

   a. hits   **b.** failures   **c.** award winners

4. She believes that everyone is **unique**.

   a. different   **b.** special   **c.** similar

>> **B.** Write an antonym for each word in the box below. Use a dictionary if needed.

Word	Antonym
stupid	
unfriendly	
calm	
huge	

>> **C.** Write two sentences that include both a word and its antonym.

1. _____

2. _____

📖 **Journal** Look for three words in the selection. Write these words in your journal, along with their antonyms.

LA.A.1.3.4.7.3 Uses a graphic organizer to clarify the meaning of text
LA.A.2.3.1.7.1 Extends the expectations of the sixth grade with increasingly complex reading texts and assignments and tasks

Name _____

Draw Conclusions

> **A.** Reread the selection. Find two facts that support the conclusion. Then fill in the chart.

> When you **draw conclusions**, you make decisions about a story and its characters based on facts or details from the story.

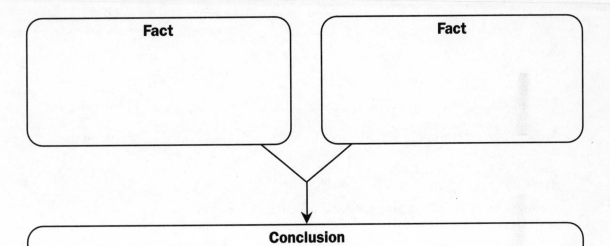

Fact

Fact

Conclusion

Cassandra Walker devotes her life to getting the message out about oneself and reaching one's goals.

> **B.** Cassandra Walker wrote, "You are created to be unique, and unique is what you are." Provide two facts from your own life and experience that support this conclusion.

1. Fact: _____

_____

2. Fact: _____

_____

Cassandra Walker

LA.D.1.3.1.7.1 Identifies patterns and rules found in the English language

Name _____

Words With -er, -est

>> **A.** Read each pair of sentences. Then look at the word in parentheses ( ). Write the proper form of the word in the blank.

> The comparative form of an adjective is used to **compare** two things. Form the comparative by adding the suffix -er (example: *taller*). The superlative form is used to compare three or more things. Form the superlative form by adding the suffix -est (example: *tallest*).

1. Cassandra showed a lot of understanding.

   She was _____ than other kids her age. (wise)

2. She compared herself to a gazelle. A gazelle is _____ than a turtle. (quick)

3. He likes to insult others. He is the _____ person I know. (mean)

4. She didn't get straight A's. She was not the _____ person in the class. (smart)

5. The girl thanked Cassandra for giving her strength. She was _____ now as a result of meeting Cassandra Walker. (strong)

>> **B.** Read each word. Then write the word in the comparative and superlative form.

	Comparative	Superlative
1. sweet	_____	_____
2. small	_____	_____
3. long	_____	_____
4. full	_____	_____

Activity Tell your class about someone you admire. Use comparative and superlative adjectives in your description.

Cassandra Walker

Name _____

Common and Proper Nouns

> **Proper nouns** name a particular person, place, or thing. You should always capitalize proper nouns. **Common nouns** refer to people, places, or things in general and are not capitalized.

>> A. Underline all the common nouns in the following sentences.

1. Cassandra wanted to go to college.
2. Cassandra decided to become a writer.
3. Cassandra worked as a reporter for a newspaper in Chicago.
4. Cassandra's job involved working on television for children.
5. The lesson Cassandra learned was "never give up."

>> B. Find the proper nouns in the sentences below. Underline each letter that should be capitalized.

1. In high school, cassandra took an honors class.
2. On the *oprah winfrey show,* she answered all of oprah's questions.
3. She was proud to be an african american and treasured her heritage.
4. She got inspired after reading *blubber* by judy blume.
5. After graduating, cassandra worked for the chicago heights *star*.

>> C. Write two sentences, one that includes a proper noun and one that includes a common noun.

1. _____

2. _____

Cassandra Walker

Name _____

Be a Career Counselor

Match each person's interests with the duties described in the ads.

>> Look again at the help-wanted ads on page 222 of your book as you complete this activity.

Reread the ads to help you choose the job that suits each person. Fill in the chart with your responses.

1. Karen wants to work outdoors.

2. Ray wants to learn to cook.

3. Jason loves kids.

Name	Best Job Option	Reason

Cassandra Walker

Name _____

Words, Words, Words

> startled: surprised
>
> chant: a phrase said or sung over and over again
>
> invasion: taking over a country by armed force
>
> writhing: twisting and turning in pain
>
> oath: a serious promise
>
> interpret: explain the meaning of; translate

>> **A.** Complete each sentence with a vocabulary word. Write the word in the blank.

1. When I slammed my finger in the door, I was _____ in pain.

2. The _____ began when the soldiers crossed the border.

3. I took an _____ not to tell my friend's secret.

4. The screeching siren _____ me as the ambulance whizzed by.

5. Paul joined in to repeat a familiar _____.

6. Joe's ability to speak two languages allowed him to _____ both Navajo and English.

>> **B.** Match the situation to a vocabulary word. Write the letter of the situation on the line.

Vocabulary Word	Situation
_____ **1.** chant	**a.** A country attacks another country.
_____ **2.** invasion	**b.** A person jumped because of a loud noise.
_____ **3.** oath	**c.** A person can explain a code.
_____ **4.** writhing	**d.** A phrase is repeated again and again.
_____ **5.** startled	**e.** A pledge to tell the truth is made.
_____ **6.** interpret	**f.** A person is squirming in terrible discomfort.

Journal Find three words in the newspaper about war or the military. Write them in your journal.

LA.D.2.3.2.7.1 Uses figurative language techniques

Name _____

Denotation/ Connotation

> The **denotation** of a word is its actual meaning. The **connotation** of a word is its suggested meaning or the feelings and images that the word creates.

>> **A.** Complete each sentence by writing the word or phrase with the more positive or respectful connotation on the line.

1. Joe's family felt connected to their _____. **(ancestors, dead relatives)**

2. His family had lived in _____ for many years. **(agreement, harmony)**

3. The teacher should have _____ Paul out of the room. **(escorted, dragged)**

4. The food tasted _____ to the boys. **(weird, unusual)**

5. Many of the family's traditions were _____. **(nice, sacred)**

>> **B.** Write a word or phrase from the box that has a stronger connotation than each numbered word.

> **fascinated**   **tiny**   **longed for**   **cheered**   **seize**

1. clapped   _____

2. small   _____

3. missed   _____

4. take   _____

5. interested   _____

 Journal Find two other words in a novel or short story that have a clear connotation. Write these words in your journal.

My Native Tongue

LA.A.1.3.4.7.3 Uses a graphic organizer to clarify the meaning of text

Name _____

Analyze Setting

> The **setting** is the time and place in which story takes place.

▶▶ A. Look again at Scenes Five and Nine from *My Native Tongue*. Then complete the chart.

Scene	Details about the setting	How the setting affects Joe
Scene Five		
Scene Nine		

▶▶ B. Choose another scene from *My Native Tongue*. Describe the setting and explain how it affects the characters or the events of the play

_____

_____

_____

_____

_____

_____

Name _____

Easily Confused Words

Some words are **easily confused** with other words because of their spelling or their pronunciation.

>> **A.** Underline the correct word to complete each sentence.

1. The Marines knew that if they lost this battle, they would **(lose, loose)** the war.
2. Joe's family lived in the hot, dry **(desert, dessert)**.
3. Joe wanted to do what was **(write, right)**.
4. Some said it wasn't **(our, are)** war to fight.
5. During the attack, we **(past, passed)** through a field of grass.

>> **B.** Write a sentence for each word in parentheses () that you did not underline in Part A.

1. _____
2. _____
3. _____
4. _____
5. _____

>> **C.** Read each question. Write the correct answer on the line.

1. Which word is the opposite of the word *tight?* _____ **(lose, loose)**
2. Which word would you find on a menu? _____ **(desert, dessert)**
3. Which word means *not the present or the future?* _____ **(past, passed)**

⬤ **Activity** Think of other pairs of easily confused words. Tell a partner how you remember which one is which.

My Native Tongue

Name _____

Prepositions

>> **A.** Underline the prepositions in the sentences below. The first one has been done for you.

> A **preposition** is a word such as *into*, *against*, *with*, *to*, *of*, and *before* that shows the relationship of a noun or pronoun to another word in the sentence. A prepositional phrase modifies a noun or a verb. It contains a preposition and a noun.

   1. A teacher yelled something <u>at</u> Paul.

   2. My mother's eyes filled with tears.

   3. We will land on the beach.

   4. All is beautiful behind me.

   5. Paul and I tried to run through the water.

>> **B.** Complete each sentence with a prepositional phrase.

   1. The textbook fell _____.

   2. We walked _____.

   3. The children rode _____.

   4. Jeremy and Jamie played ball _____.

   5. They ate dinner _____.

>> **C.** Write three sentences with prepositions on the lines. Circle the prepositions.

   1. _____

   2. _____

   3. _____

LA.A.2.3.5.7.2 Compiles, organizes, and interprets information for a variety of purposes

Name _____

Go Shopping

>> Look again at the catalog page on page 238 of your book as you complete this activity.

You have lots of gifts to buy. Use the order form below. Fill it out with everything on your list: 1 olive pullover jacket, medium; 3 baseball caps; 2 canary sweatshirts, large; 3 just plain red backpacks; 1 ivory rollneck sweater, child's medium.

> Be sure to fill in the grand total of your order, including the postage and handling charge.

Item Number	Size	Color	Price	How Many	Total Price

POSTAGE & HANDLING	
Price of Order	Charge
Up to $75	$5.00
$75.01 to $125	$6.00
$125.01 to $175	$7.00
Over $175	$9.00

Total Price of Order	
Postage & Handling	
Grand Total	

LA.A.1.3.2.7.2 Uses context clues to interpret the meaning of what is read

Name _____

Words, Words, Words

> **sickly:** weak and often ill
>
> **despondent:** miserable and depressed
>
> **exhilarated:** excited and thrilled
>
> **lively:** active and full of life
>
> **constantly:** all the time
>
> **attend:** go to

>> A. Fill in each blank with the word from the box that best fits the clue.

1. Wilma felt this way when she was unhappy for a long time. _____

2. This is what Wilma wanted to do about going to school. _____

3. This is the kind of active girl Wilma was before she got polio. _____

4. This is how often Wilma practiced her leg exercises. _____

5. When Wilma got lots of childhood illnesses, people called her this.

_____

6. Wilma felt this way after winning two Olympic gold medals. _____

>> B. What would you like to ask your favorite athlete? Write three questions. Use one vocabulary word in each sentence.

1. _____

2. _____

3. _____

Journal Find three words about illness in the selection. Write them in your journal.

LA.A.1.3.3.7.1 Extends the vocabulary-building expectations of the sixth grade using seventh grade or higher vocabulary

Name _____

Multiple-Meaning Words

> Many words you know can have several different meanings. These words are called **multiple-meaning words**.

>> **A.** Read the words below. Then fill in the blanks to use each word two different ways in the same sentence.

> brace   watch   place   treats

1. The referee checked his _____ to see how much more time they had left to _____ the race.

2. The doctor who _____ the patients gives all the children _____.

3. The people had to _____ themselves as they watched the girl take off her _____ and walk.

4. Wilma stood in the _____ where the first _____ winner is awarded the gold medal.

>> **B.** Circle the meaning that fits the way the word in bold is used in the sentence.

1. Wilma walked past each **row** of seats.

   a. chair   **b.** to move a boat   **c.** line

2. They went to the nearest hospital that would **treat** her illness.

   a. care for   **b.** write about   **c.** delicious snack

3. It seemed that Wilma was always preparing for a **race**.

   a. running contest   **b.** classification of people   **c.** run fast

Journal Look for three multiple-meaning words in the selection. Write these in your journal. Include a definition based on the way each word is used in the selection.

LA.A.1.3.4.7.3 Uses a graphic organizer to clarify the meaning of text
LA.A.2.3.1.7.1 Extends the expectations of the sixth grade with increasingly complex reading texts and assignments and tasks

Name _____

Main Idea

> **A.** Reread pages 253–258. Then fill in the chart with details that support the main idea.

The **main idea** is the most important idea. Details support, or tell more about the main idea.

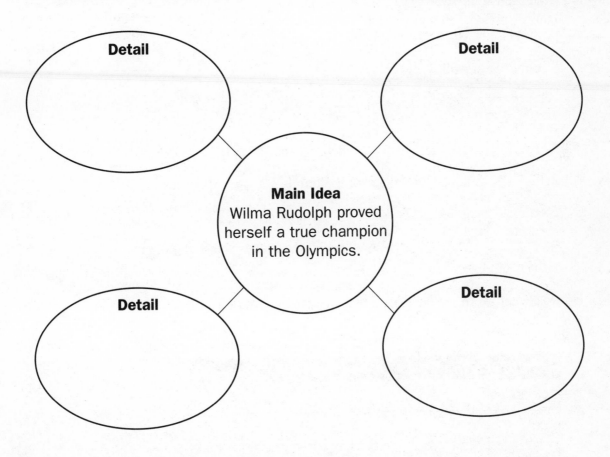

Detail

Detail

Main Idea
Wilma Rudolph proved herself a true champion in the Olympics.

Detail

Detail

> **B.** Write a sentence that tells another main idea about Wilma Rudolph. Then write a sentence containing a detail that supports your idea.

1. _____

_____

2. _____

_____

Wilma Unlimited

Name _____

Gerunds

>> **A.** Read the verbs in the box. Then fill in the blanks with gerunds based on those verbs.

play	work
cook	walk

> A **gerund** is an *-ing* form of a verb that acts as a noun in a sentence. (For example, sing is a verb, but in the following sentence it is a gerund and acts as a noun: Singing gives her great joy.)

1. _____ hard is sometimes the secret of success.

2. _____ dinner for the family was one of her tasks.

3. _____ basketball was important to Wilma.

4. _____ step-by-step without braces was a major achievement.

>> **B.** Read each word on the chart. Then write the gerund form of the word in the chart.

Verb	Gerund
clean	
talk	
laugh	
sing	
walk	

Journal Tell a partner about a sport you enjoy. Use at least three gerunds.

Name _____

Adverbs That Tell Where and When

> **Adverbs** are words that modify a verb, an adjective, or another adverb. Some adverbs tell *where* or *when* an action occurs.

>> A. Underline the adverb that tells where or when in each sentence. The first one has been done for you.

1. Lately, she wasn't running fast.
2. The fact that she won sank in afterwards.
3. The day of the meet came up suddenly.
4. She wanted to take her brace off now.
5. First she planned how she would win the race.
6. Soon it was time to run.
7. Where will the Olympics be held?
8. The Rudolphs liked to get to church early.
9. She looked outside at the children playing.
10. Wilma had to stay inside and do her exercises.

>> B. Write a sentence using each adverb.

1. (behind) _____

_____

2. (tomorrow) _____

_____

3. (finally) _____

_____

LA.A.2.3.5.7.2 Compiles, organizes, and interprets information for a variety of purposes

Name _____

Write a Receipt

>> Look again at the sales receipt on page 266 of your book as you complete this activity.

Create a receipt from your favorite store for the following shopping spree:

- $50 down jacket

- $25 swimsuit

- $30 ski goggles

- $10 swim goggles

The sales tax on these items is 5%.

> Remember to add the sales tax to your subtotal. The sales tax here is 5%. So multiply your subtotal by .05.

Store	
Items	
Subtotal	
Tax	
TOTAL	

Wilma Unlimited

Name _____

Words, Words, Words

> burrows: digs a tunnel or hole
>
> stimulate: to encourage something to grow or develop
>
> absorb: to take in
>
> prescription: medicine that is ordered by a doctor
>
> moist: slightly wet
>
> parasites: living organisms that feed off their hosts

>> **A.** Use one of the words from the box to fill in each blank.

The student had a fever. She complained about a rash, feeling wet and

(1) _____. A doctor confirmed she had been infected by

(2) _____ found in food. This particular organism

(3) _____ into the stomach lining. There it will (4) _____

nutrients from the food the student eats, which will (5) _____ the growth

of the parasite. Fortunately, the doctor gave the student a (6) _____ for

a medication.

>> **B.** Write three sentences using a different word from the box above for each sentence.

1. _____

_____

2. _____

_____

3. _____

Journal Look for three other words in your book that might be used in
a discussion of bugs that live in the human body. Write the words in
your journal.

Body Bugs

Name _____

Specialized Vocabulary

>> **A.** Use context clues to help you figure out the meaning of each underlined word. Then write the meaning of the word in the blank.

> When a word is not familiar to you, **context clues** can often help you figure out its meaning. This skill can help when reading selections with **specialized vocabulary**, such as science.

1. The nurse combs students' hair to make sure she has found all the unhatched <u>nits</u>. _____

2. The head louse is one of many tiny organisms that has <u>mouthparts</u> designed for sucking blood. _____

3. Once the tapeworm has reached a person's stomach lining, it forms a <u>cyst</u> around itself. _____

4. Some of these creatures are as tiny as 2 or 3 <u>microns</u>. _____

5. Because the ringworm is a fungus, the only medicine that will treat the infection is an <u>antifungal</u> cream. _____

6. The <u>follicle</u> mite lives around the bottom of your eyelashes. _____

>> **B.** Write three original sentences about "Body Bugs." Use the specialized word in parentheses.

1. (nits) _____

2. (follicles) _____

3. (microns) _____

📓 **Journal** Find other specialized vocabulary terms from the two selections. In your journal, write two words and their meanings.

Name _____

Compare and Contrast

>> **A.** Compare and contrast head lice and tapeworms. Write your answers in the appropriate part of the chart below.

To **compare** is to find out how two things are alike. To **contrast** means to find their differences.

Parasites

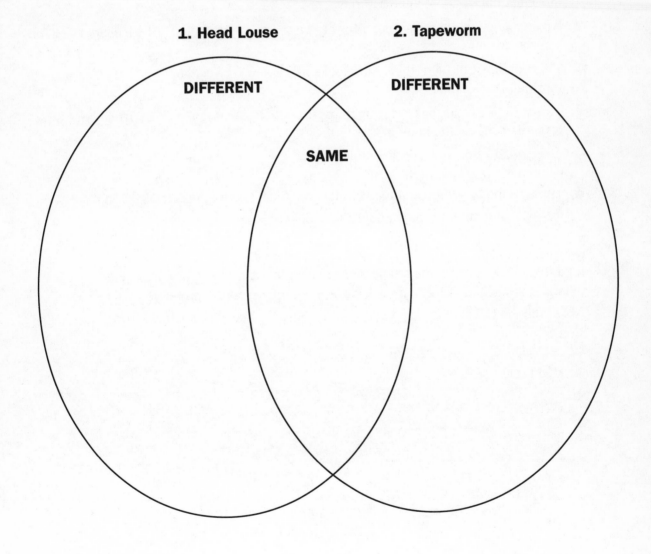

1. Head Louse

2. Tapeworm

DIFFERENT

DIFFERENT

SAME

Name _____

Irregular Plurals

>> **A.** Tell whether each noun in dark type (**boldface**) has a regular or an irregular plural by checking the correct box.

> The plurals of nouns are usually formed by adding -s or -es. Some words, however, have **irregular plurals** (for example, *child/children*).

1. The **child** had a huge tapeworm in her intestinal tract. □ Regular □ Irregular

2. An action as simple as sharing a **towel** can spread some of these infections. □ Regular □ Irregular

3. The mouthpart of the follicle mite looks like a **tooth** and pierces the skin. □ Regular □ Irregular

4. This **mite** is one of the tiniest creatures to make its home in the body. □ Regular □ Irregular

5. A **fungus** like the one causing athlete's foot can remain in the body for years. □ Regular □ Irregular

6. The head **louse** is becoming more common now that hat sales among young people have grown. □ Regular □ Irregular

>> **B.** Find two other words in the article or elsewhere in your book that have irregular plurals. Use the plural form of each word in a sentence about protecting yourself from body bugs.

1. _____

_____

2. _____

_____

⬤ **Activity** Choose two words from this page that have irregular plural forms. Use them in a conversation with a partner.

Name _____

Vary Sentence Beginnings

> To avoid writing that sounds the same, good writers **vary sentence beginnings**. They use different ways of beginning their sentences.

>> Vary sentence beginnings by:

- Starting with an adverb.
  Sometimes, a body rash can be the sign of an infestation.

- Starting with a clause.
  If you spot a head louse, you should get treatment.

- Starting with a prepositional phrase.
  On his desk was a book on follicle mites.

>> **A.** Rewrite each sentence by changing the beginning or reordering the words.

1. We get to look at bugs under a microscope occasionally.

_____

2. You can develop a rash if you get itch mites.

_____

3. The doctor found follicle mites near the bottom of her eye lashes.

_____

4. We studied athlete's foot fungus later in the week.

_____

>> **B.** Write three original sentences about body bugs. Each sentence should have a different beginning.

1. _____

2. _____

3. _____

Body Bugs

Name _____

Have a Snack

>> Look again at the nutrition labels on page 278 of your book as you complete this activity.

Collect labels from two of your favorite snacks. Then fill in the chart below with information from the nutrition labels on the snacks.

To log the nutritional content of your snacks, save the packaging or copy down the important information in a notebook.

	Snack 1		Snack 2	
	grams	% Daily Value	grams	% Daily Value
Fat				
Sodium				
Protein				
Sugar				
Fiber				
Calcium				
Vitamin A				
Vitamin C				

Name _____

Words, Words, Words

> **summit:** very top
> **inevitable:** sure to happen
> **oxygen:** a colorless gas found in the air
> **fatigue:** great tiredness
> **steep:** sharply sloping up or down
> **pilgrimage:** a long journey in search of something

>> **A.** Use one of the words from the box to fill in each blank.

The climber traveled so far that he felt he was on a (1) _____ to

reach the (2) _____ of the mountain. As he climbed, the air grew

thinner, requiring him to use more (3) _____ from his tank. As he

climbed straight up the (4) _____ mountain he saw the storm front

waiting to the east. A great (5) _____ overcame him, and he

became more and more tired. But despite the storm and his exhaustion he knew reaching

the mountain top was (6) _____.

>> **B.** Fill in the blank with the correct vocabulary word.

1. The climber had a tank of _____ that enabled him to climb the

tall peak.

2. Because the snow was so weak, it was _____ that there would soon

be an avalanche.

3. _____ prevented the worn-out climbers from reaching the summit.

Journal Look for three other words in your book that might be used in
a discussion of mountain climbing.

Name _____

Context Clues

>> **A.** Draw a circle around words or phrases that help you figure out the meaning of the underlined word. Write the meaning in the space provided.

> An unfamiliar word is a word you do not know. Use **context clues**—the words around it—to find the meaning of the unfamiliar word.

1. On his way down the mountain, Mark <u>traversed</u> many of the same trails he had passed over on the way up.

_____

2. The <u>whiteout</u> was caused by white clouds descending on the snow.

_____

3. A climber fills her <u>rucksack</u> with camping gear and food before putting it on her back.

_____

4. Mark had a nagging cough that left him <u>hacking</u> so much that he was unable to speak.

_____

>> **B.** Figure out the meaning of the words from their context in the story. Write their meanings below.

1. (corporate, p. 281) _____

_____

2. (component, p. 282) _____

_____

3. (windchill, p. 282) _____

_____

📓 **Journal** Find three other sentences in Mark's journal that contain an unfamiliar word defined by its context. Write the word and its meanings in your journal. Check your definitions in a dictionary.

Within Reach: My Everest Story

Name _____

Sequence of Events

>> Starting with May 11, rewrite the events in proper sequence. Use the chart to order the events.

> A **sequence of events** is the order in which events happen. Time-order words, such as *later, then*, and *after,* can also help you keep track of the order.

A. Finally, Mark sends a message to his mother.

B. Then, Mark discovers that Scott Fischer has died.

C. Then, Mark, Graham, and Jabion decide to go down because of the storm. **D.** Mark reaches Camp Three. **E.** Next, Mark discovers nine people are missing. **F.** First, Pasang, one of the Sherpas leaves.

EVENT

↓

EVENT

↓

EVENT

↓

EVENT

↓

EVENT

↓

EVENT

Name _____

Action Words

>> **A.** Replace the underlined word or words with a livelier action word from the box.

> Writers often use strong verbs and other **action words** to make the reading more lively.

> huddle   howls   seep   doze   stumble

1. The wind <u>sounds</u> through the mountain passes, signaling the approach of a storm.

_____

2. Soon the snow comes, and we <u>try to go</u> forward through the whiteout.

_____

3. We <u>sleep for little bits of time</u>, then wake again suddenly, thinking we have heard an important noise outside. _____

4. As we <u>group together</u> in our tent, waiting out the storm, questions arise.

_____

>> **B.** Use a strong action verb from the box to complete each sentence.

> scramble   glows   numbs   roars

1. We _____ quickly up the mountain.

2. The wind _____ in our ears.

3. The cold air _____ our faces and fingers.

4. Friendly light _____ from the tents in the distance.

◯ **Activity** Talk with a partner about an activity you like to participate in. Use action words in your conversation.

Within Reach: My Everest Story

Name _____

Transitional Words

>> **A.** Circle the transitional words and phrases in the following sentences.

> **Transitional words** help link ideas and signal when changes happen. They help readers follow along easily when reading. Some examples of transitional words and phrases include *suddenly*, *once*, and *by the time*.

1. Suddenly, an unexpected storm rushes in.

2. Soon, I make camp to get some rest.

3. The next morning, a Sherpa guide begins to pack.

4. Once we awaken, we find that he has gone.

5. The rest of our team is making breakfast by the time I emerge from my tent.

6. The moment we resume our climb, the wind begins to howl.

>> **B.** Use transitional words to write three sentences about "Within Reach: My Everest Story."

1. _____
   _____

2. _____
   _____

3. _____
   _____

LA.A.2.3.5.7.2 Compiles, organizes, and interprets information for a variety of purposes

Name _____

Plan Your Budget

To help you fill out the chart, keep a log of how you spend your money for one week.

>> Look again at the weekly budget on page 290 of your book as you complete this activity.

Do you work or get an allowance? What is your weekly net income? What are your fixed expenses? What else do you spend money on? Plan a weekly budget for yourself. Record all your income and expenses on the chart below. Suppose you want to save money. Which expenses could you cut?

WEEKLY NET INCOME	
net income	
FIXED EXPENSES	
total fixed expenses	
FLEXIBLE EXPENSES	
total flexible expenses	
SAVINGS	
total savings	

Possible expenses to cut: _____

_____

Name _____

Words, Words, Words

> **leagues:** measures of distance each marking about three miles
> **loyal:** faithful, supportive
> **harpoon:** a long spear attached to a rope used in whaling
> **fibers:** slender threads of cotton, wool, or other material
> **pumps:** machines that force liquid or gas from one place to another
> **rammed:** struck or ran into with great force

>> **A.** Find the missing words. Fill in each blank with a word from the box.

The (1) _____ of the ship's sail stretched in the wind. The captain knew

he could count on his (2) _____ crew. The ship had traveled for 20

(3) _____ when the first mate saw something huge coming toward them.

He threw a (4) _____ at it, but the spear just bounced off. Suddenly the

thing (5) _____ into the ship, tearing a hole in its side. Would the ship's

(6) _____ be able to get rid of the water before everyone drowned?

>> **B.** Read each sentence. Then, write an answer on the line.

1. Name something you could find **fibers** in. _____

2. Estimate how many **leagues** there are between your home and school.

_____

3. Name someone you are **loyal** to. _____

4. Write something you could catch with a **harpoon**. _____

5. Name something that **pumps** air or liquid every day. _____

Journal Look for three other words in the selection that might be used in a
discussion of sea voyages and adventures. Write them in your journal.

Word Study

LA.A.1.3.2.7.1 Uses knowledge of word parts to determine the meaning of unfamiliar words in a literary or informative text

Name _____

Compound Words

>> **A.** Underline the compound word in each sentence. Draw a line between the two smaller words in each compound word. Then write the meaning of the word.

> **Compound words** are words made up of two smaller words. You can often figure out the meaning of a compound word by looking at the meanings of the two smaller words.

1. The newspapers reported another mysterious accident.

_____

2. Some said that the shipwrecks were caused by a monster.

_____

3. A giant wave pulled Professor Aronnax overboard.

_____

4. The broken ship filled with seawater.

_____

5. The captain kept his diary dry in a waterproof box.

_____

>> **B.** Choose three compound words from the box. Use each in an original sentence about *20,000 Leagues Under the Sea*.

> **underwater   anywhere   anyone   undersea   underside**

1. _____

2. _____

3. _____

Journal Look in a dictionary for other compound words that begin with *any* or *under*. Write three of them in your journal, along with their definitions.

LA.A.1.3.4.7.3 Uses a graphic organizer to clarify the meaning of text
LA.A.2.3.1.7.1 Extends the expectations of the sixth grade with increasingly complex reading texts and assignments and tasks

Name _____

Analyze Plot

>> Reread pages 308–309 of *20,000 Leagues Under the Sea*. Then complete this chart to keep track of what Professor Aronnax and his friends do as they finally try to escape.

The **plot** is the sequence of events that takes place in a story. The plot usually focuses on a problem that the main character faces and tries to solve. The turning point is the moment when his or her fate seems to change.

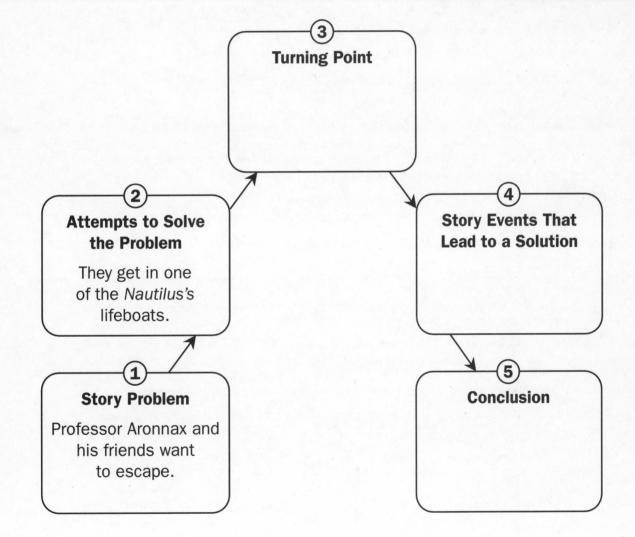

3 Turning Point

2 Attempts to Solve the Problem

They get in one of the *Nautilus's* lifeboats.

4 Story Events That Lead to a Solution

1 Story Problem

Professor Aronnax and his friends want to escape.

5 Conclusion

Name _____

Exclamations

>> **A.** Circle the number in front of each sentence that uses exclamations correctly. Think about how the speaker is talking.

> An **exclamation** is an expression of surprise or strong emotion. An exclamation mark signals that a sentence or phrase is to be read with emphasis or excitement.

1. "How strange!" he cried out.

2. "Where do you get your money!" asked the Professor, yawning.

3. "The oxygen comes from these tanks!" he explained calmly.

4. "It's some kind of whale!" the first mate said in amazement.

5. "It's the monster!" the sailors screamed.

>> **B.** What would you say in the following situations? Write an exclamation for each.

1. You just ran into your best friend at the store. It's during summer vacation and you haven't seen each other for weeks.

_____

2. You open a birthday present from your family. It's something you've always wanted.

_____

3. You are baby-sitting and look under the bed to prove that there's nothing there. Big yellow eyes stare back at you.

_____

4. You open an envelope and discover you have won the grand prize.

_____

Activity Read your sentences aloud to your partner. Remember to express emotion or surprise. Then read them without the exclamation mark and discuss any differences in meaning you detect.

Name _____

Dialogue and Quotation Marks

> Words spoken by one character to another are known as **dialogue**. Lines of dialogue are set off by **quotation marks** ("").

>> **A.** Draw one line under the dialogue or spoken words. Draw two lines under the words that show who is speaking and how they are talking. The first one is an example.

1. "Professor, could I interest you in a tour of the ship?" <u>Nemo asked.</u>
2. "Of course!" he replied.
3. "All our food is from the sea," Nemo explained. "We eat fish and vegetables from undersea farms."
4. Professor Aronnax asked, "Where do you get the money to pay for all this?"
5. "We collect gold from shipwrecks," he answered.

>> **B.** Place quotations marks around the dialogue in the sentences below.

1. You have no right to keep us here, Professor Aronnax said.
2. I can do whatever I like, Nemo replied. This is my ship.
3. The professor asked nervously, What are you planning to do with us?
4. Suddenly a member of his crew shouted, Captain, we have spotted a ship!
5. Nemo stood up and said, I haven't decided your fate, Professor. Then he turned and left abruptly.

>> **C.** Imagine a dialogue between Professor Aronnax and either Conseil or Ned when they reach land. Use quotation marks to set off what they say.

_____

_____

_____

_____

Name _____

Fill It Out

>> Look again at the mail form on page 312 of your book as you complete this activity.

It's Wednesday. Joe Pito wants his pictures by Friday. He wants to pay for shipping with his credit card, number 3984 8423, which expires 11/11. The order fits in a Speedy Ship box and weighs four ounces. It's worth about $40. Fill out sections 3–6 in the form below.

> Since you are responsible for filling out only half of the shipping form, the other half has not been included.

---

3 Express Service

☐ Overnight Rush (next morning*)   ☐ Regular Overnight*

☐ 2nd day (day after tomorrow*)
  *Business days only

4 Packaging

☐ Speedy Ship letter ☐ Speedy Ship Box ☐ Customer's Packaging

5 Special

☐ Saturday Delivery   ☐ Sunday Delivery   ☐ Hold at Speedy Ship Office

Speedy Ship will not ship dangerous goods.

6 Payment/Billing Information

Bill: ☐ Sender   ☐ Recipient   ☐ Credit Card   ☐ Cash/Check

Speedy Ship Acct. No. _____

Credit Card. No. _____ Exp. Date _____

Number of Packages _____ Total Weight _____ Total Value _____

Name _____

Words, Words, Words

> **achievements:** things done successfully with great effort or courage
> **confidence:** a belief in one's own ability
> **prejudice:** an unfair opinion about a group of people based on their race or religion
> **enormous:** very large
> **hardships:** conditions that one suffers through
> **contribution:** one's part in achieving or completing something

>> **A.** Fill in each blank with a word from the box.

   1. One of America's greatest _____ was completing the Transcontinental Railroad.

   2. The _____ job reached from coast to coast.

   3. Charles Crocker had the _____ to complete such a project.

   4. In spite of many terrible _____, Chinese workers continued to lay track.

   5. Many Americans treated the Chinese unfairly and held a _____ against them because they seemed different.

   6. The Chinese workers made a valuable _____.

>> **B.** Write three questions you would like to ask a "Rosie." Use one vocabulary word in each.

   1. _____

   2. _____

   3. _____

 **Journal** Find three words about hardship in a newspaper. Write them in your journal.

Word Study

LA.A.1.3.2.7.1 Uses knowledge of word parts to determine the meaning of unfamiliar words in a literary or informative text

Name _____

Roots

>> **A.** Circle the word in each sentence below that uses a root listed in the box.

> A **root** is a word or word part from Latin or another language that is used to build English words. One example of a root is *credit*, which means, "to believe."

scend = to climb	**explo** = to drive out by clapping
super = over, above	
mem = mindful	**credit** = to believe

1. The "Rosies" who aided the war effort had many memories to share.

2. Railroad workers were hurt in the explosion.

3. She was the first woman to become supervisor of the factory.

4. The railroad workers descended from the mountaintop to the valley floor.

5. The vaqueros performed incredible feats on the cattle drives.

>> **B.** Read each numbered word below. Think of other words that have the same root and write them on the line. You may use a dictionary for help.

1. superior _____

2. memory _____

3. explode _____

> **Journal** Look for two additional words whose roots can be used to make another word you know. Write these words in your journal.

Comprehension

LA.A.1.3.4.7.2 Restates or paraphrases text by summarizing
LA.A.2.3.1.7.1 Extends the expectations of the sixth grade with increasingly complex reading texts and assignments and tasks

Name _____

Summarize

▶▶ Look again at pages 320–321. Summarize the role the Chinese played in building the railroad.

A **summary** tells the most important facts about a topic. When you write a summary, you express the key details in your own words.

Important Detail or Event

The Chinese worked under harsh weather conditions.

Important Detail or Event

Important Detail or Event

Important Detail or Event

Summary

They Built America

Name _____

Sensory Words

> **A.** Use a word from the box to complete each sentence below.

> **Sensory words** are words and details that appeal to the five senses: sight, smell, hearing, taste, and touch.

scorching	rough	cold
towering	sweet	heat

1. The _____ heat made them feel as if they were on fire.

2. The _____ smell of flower blossoms was carried on the wind.

3. The wool sweater felt itchy and _____ on her skin.

4. The icy _____ winter winds howled at night.

5. The summer _____ made them very thirsty.

> **B.** Read each word in the list. Identify the sense it most appeals to.

1. scorching _____

2. salty _____

3. perfume _____

4. beautiful _____

5. roar _____

⬤ **Activity** Describe your favorite meal to a partner. Use words that appeal to the senses in your description.

They Built America

Name _____

Subject and Predicate

>> **A.** Underline the simple subject in each of the following sentences. The first one has been done for you.

> The simple **subject** of a sentence is the noun or pronoun that tells who or what the sentence is about.
> The simple **predicate** is the verb that tells what the subject does or is.

1. The <u>herds</u> moved north to Spanish-controlled Texas and California.
2. John Wayne played a cowboy in many movies.
3. The vaqueros liked to sing songs like "Cielito Lindo."
4. The American cowboy inherited a lot of words from the vaqueros.
5. Some words have their origins in Spanish.

>> **B.** Underline the simple predicate in the following sentences. The first one has been done for you.

1. The attack on Pearl Harbor <u>plunged</u> the United States into war.
2. As a result, women got jobs in the factories.
3. People considered most jobs unladylike.
4. Women became firefighters and bus drivers.
5. After the war, most women lost their jobs.

>> **C.** Write one sentence about each of the three nonfiction stories in the selection. Underline the simple subject and predicate in your sentences.

1. _____

2. _____

3. _____

LA.D.2.3.3.7.2 Recognizes differences between propaganda and logical reasoning strategies
LA.A.2.3.3.7.1 Identifies persuasive and propaganda techniques in text
LA.A.2.3.3.7.2 Delineates the strengths and weaknesses of an argument

Name _____

Buyer Beware

Make sure you always read the fine print on ads!

>> Look again at the ads on page 324 of your book as you complete this activity.

Find a newspaper or magazine and choose three ads. Read them carefully. Do you think the deals they are offering are bargains or not? List your reasons in the chart below

What's the Ad for?	Is It a Bargain?	Why or Why Not?

LA.A.1.3.1.7.1 Extends and applies previously learned prereading knowledge and skills of the sixth grade with increasingly complex reading selections and assignments and tasks

Name _____

Previewing

>> Use this page as you preview "Leatherback Sea Turtles." Answer the questions that follow.

To **preview**, look at the title, section heads, photographs, illustrations, and graphic aids. Then, use prior knowledge to make predictions and generate questions about the text.

1. Skim through the screens of "Leatherback Sea Turtles." List some topics the feature will discuss.

_____

_____

_____

2. Jot down anything you already know about the subject of "Leatherback Sea Turtles."

_____

_____

_____

3. Make a prediction about what you will learn by reading the selection.

_____

_____

_____

4. Write down a question you would like to have answered by your reading of "Leatherback Sea Turtles."

_____

_____

_____

Leatherback Sea Turtles

Name _____

Sum It Up

> **hatcheries:** places where fish, chicken, or turtle eggs are hatched
> **endangered:** in danger of becoming extinct or no longer existing
> **steer:** to guide in a particular direction
> **reptiles:** cold-blooded animals that have backbones, are covered with scales or hard plates, breathe with lungs, and reproduce by laying eggs
> **predators:** animals that live by hunting other animals for food
> **hatchlings:** young fish, reptiles, or birds that have recently emerged from eggs
> **flippers:** the flat limbs of a sea creature that help it to swim

>> Show what you know about the world's largest turtles. Complete the summary below by filling in the blanks with words from the box above.

Leatherback turtles are one of the oldest _____ on earth. These 1,000 pound turtles are excellent swimmers. Their front _____ work as paddles. They use the ones in back to _____.

Female leatherbacks come ashore to nest, laying as many as 100 eggs at a time. Scientists, trying to help these _____ creatures, sometimes move the eggs. They take them to _____, where the _____ have a better chance to survive. Leatherbacks born in a nest wait until night to head for the water. If they cross the sand during the day, they risk being eaten by _____.

Leatherback Sea Turtles

Name _____

Taking Notes

>> Complete this page to take notes while you read "Rachel and Jackie Robinson: A Time Line." Some notes have already been written in.

> When you **take notes** about a text, you record important information in an organized way. Later, you can review this information to help you remember what you've read.

Title: "Rachel and Jackie Robinson: A Time Line."

Topic: Events in Rachel and Jackie's lives

Time Period	Date/Event
1910–1939	1919-Jackie born/Cairo, Georgia 1922-Rachel born/Los Angeles, California
1940s	1940-Jackie and Rachel meet
1950–1969	1950-52-children born 1957-Jackie leaves baseball, works in business/with NAACP
1970–Today	

Name _____

Sum It Up

> **subtle:** done in a hidden way
> **provocation:** the act of angering someone enough to get a response from them
> **abused:** treated badly
> **taunts:** unkind teasing to make someone angry or upset
> **discrimination:** unfair treatment of others based on differences in race
> **excels:** does something very well

▶▶ How much do you know about the life and times of Rachel and Jackie Robinson? Complete the summary below by filling in the blanks with words from the box above.

Even in high school Jackie Robinson _____ in sports. When Jackie meets his wife Rachel, he is a four-sport star at UCLA. In 1947, he becomes the first African American of the century to play in major league baseball. That year, he overcomes many obstacles. He faces both obvious _____ and more _____ racism. Nonetheless, he earns the Rookie of the Year award. Sometimes, Jackie is bothered by the _____ of fans who only want white players in the league. Even when he is verbally _____, however, he doesn't let it affect his game. He refuses to respond to _____ during 10 seasons in the league. Jackie dies in 1972. In 1973, Rachel starts a foundation in his name. Over the next two decades, it provides college scholarships to hundreds of students.

Rachel and Jackie Robinson

Name _____

Reviewing and Revising Notes

> **Reviewing and revising notes** helps you to remember the important ideas in what you read. You can also reorganize your notes for specific purposes.

>> A. Review your notes on "Spanish Roots in America." Use them to write sentences describing the events that occurred in the times and places listed below. The first sentence has been started for you.

1598 New Mexico In 1598, Don Juan de Oñate, _____

_____

1821 Mexico _____

_____

1898 Cuba _____

_____

>> B. Revise your notes to make two lists, one of events that took place in Florida and one of events that occurred in the American Southwest (including New Mexico).

Florida **Date/Event**	**American Southwest** **Date/Event**
_____	_____
_____	_____
_____	_____
_____	_____
_____	_____

Name _____

Sum It Up

> **territory:** a large area of land
>
> **route:** the road or course followed to travel from one place to another
>
> **settlement:** a town built by people who have left one place to make a home in another
>
> **cedes:** transfers from one to the other
>
> **conquer:** to defeat and take control of an enemy
>
> **voyages:** long journeys, especially across an ocean
>
> **republic:** a country in which the people have the power to elect government officials
>
> **harbor:** a place where ships dock and unload their cargo

➤➤ How much do you know about Spanish roots in the Americas?
Complete the summaries below by filling in the blanks with words
from the box above.

- Christopher Columbus reaches San Salvador while trying to find a sea

    _____ to the Far East. This is the first of his four _____

    to the Americas.

- In 1521, Hernando Cortés is able to _____ the Aztecs and seize their

    empire for Spain.

- The _____ of St. Augustine, Florida, is the oldest American city settled

    by Europeans.

- In 1845, Texas becomes an independent _____. Later, Mexico gives up

    large tracts of _____ to the U.S.

- In 1898, the *Maine* is blown up in a Cuban _____. War breaks out

    between the U.S. and Spain. Eventually, Spain _____ control of Puerto

    Rico and other places to the U.S.

Name _____

Using Graphic Organizers

>> "The Montgomery Bus Boycott" describes a series of events set in motion by Rosa Park's refusal to give up her seat. Use this sequence-of-events chain to note the *major* events in the selection. Continue the chain on a separate sheet of paper if necessary.

> **Graphic organizers** can help you to organize and remember the information and relationships contained in difficult texts.

Rosa Parks refuses to give up her seat on a Montgomery bus.	⇨	

Name _____

Sum It Up

> **violating:** breaking a rule or law
>
> **oppression:** the act of treating people in a cruel and unjust way
>
> **provoked:** annoyed someone enough to make the person angry
>
> **bail:** money given so a person can be released from jail
>
> **boycott:** to refuse to buy something or take part in something as a way of protesting
>
> **segregation:** the act or practice of keeping people or things away from the main group
>
> **harass:** to annoy or disturb someone over and over
>
> **policies:** the rules and guidelines of a company or organization
>
> **appeal:** to ask for a decision made by a court of law to be changed

>> Can you retell the story of the Montgomery bus boycott? Complete the summary below by filling in the blanks with words from the box above.

In December of 1955, _____ was the rule in Montgomery,

Alabama. _____ of the time forced black passengers to sit in the

back of the bus. One day, Rosa Parks refused to move to the back. The bus driver got the

police, and Parks was thrown in jail for _____ the law. Her friend

E.D. Nixon paid her _____ and Parks was released. African-American

leaders began a _____ of city buses. Parks's lawyer made plans to

_____ her case to the U.S. Supreme Court. Dr. Martin Luther

King Jr. spoke out against _____. White people in Montgomery

would _____ the protesters, but the protesters refused to

be _____.

Study Skills

LA.A.1.3.1.7.1 Extends and applies previously learned prereading knowledge and skills of the sixth grade with increasingly complex reading selections and assignments and tasks

Name _____

Skimming and Scanning

> Skim to decide if a resource contains the information that you are looking for. Scan to locate specific information.

>> **A. Skim** Look at each piece of information below. Then preview the selection. Put a check in the square if you think that you will find the information in the selection.

I will find:

☐ a chart showing how many immigrants arrive in the U.S each year

☐ first-hand accounts of how several young immigrants feel about their new country

☐ the age and birthplace of each immigrant

☐ maps of countries where these immigrants originally lived

>> **B. Scan** Find the answer to each question in one of the five profiles.

1. What is Vedron's favorite sport? _____

2. In what country was Margarita born? _____

3. Where does Saed live? _____

4. In what year was Van born? _____

5. Which immigrant lives in Tarrytown, New York? _____

6. Which immigrant is learning to be a mechanic? _____

Name _____

Sum It Up

> **desperate:** willing to do almost anything to change your situation
>
> **diversity:** a variety or selection of different things
>
> **dangerous:** not safe
>
> **opportunities:** chances to do something
>
> **secure:** safe and well-protected
>
> **Yugoslavia:** a country in Europe
>
> **Mexico:** a country in North America
>
> **Sudan:** a country in Africa
>
> **Haiti:** a country in the Caribbean
>
> **Vietnam:** a country in Southeast Asia

>> Tell the stories of five young immigrants. Complete the summaries
below by filling in the blanks with words from the box above.

- Margarita moved to the U.S from _____ where she never felt

  _____. Often, soldiers fired weapons near her home.

- Adriana was born in Cuernavaca, _____. There, many people

  were _____ because they had no jobs.

- Saed came here from _____. He enjoys the

  _____ of his new home.

- Van was born in _____. One day, she hopes to be a pharmacist.

  She thinks there are more _____ for her here.

- Vedron immigrated from _____. The war there made it a very

  _____ place to live.

LA.A.1.3.2.6.3 Uses note-making to clarify meaning and to illustrate organizational patterns

Name _____

Marking Up Texts

>> **A.** This screen contains some marks to highlight important information and unfamiliar vocabulary. Add two more underlines and two more vocabulary notes. Then, write a marginal note that summarizes both paragraphs.

> **Marking up a text** by underlining, circling, and making marginal notations allows you to create notes out of the text itself.

Welcome to the historic Mt. Everest expedition. <u>The team is attempting to climb the world's tallest mountain</u> and reach the summit—<u>a place no human has ever been before</u>. It has taken 16 days for <u>Edmund Hillary</u>, 13 other climbers, and 350 (porters) to reach the Tengpoche Monastery and set up a rear camp. Why are so many people taking part in this journey?

people who carry supplies

In order to reach the monastery, the team has already trekked 170 miles up the hot and humid Katmandu Valley. The terrain is smooth, and everyone is in high spirits. The Sherpas, a clan of Nepalese, watch the team curiously, and join them in celebration when they reach this first stop at Tengpoche Monastery.

>> **B.** Print out the remaining screens and mark them up yourself.

Everest: Relive the Trek

Name _____

Sum It Up

> **base camp:** a central setup of tents where food, equipment, and medical supplies are stored, as well as a relay site for climbers.
>
> **rigorous:** very harsh and uncomfortable on the body
>
> **crevasses:** deep open cracks in a glacier
>
> **crampons:** metal frames with spikes that are worn on hiking boots for ice climbs
>
> **summit:** the highest point
>
> **ice picks:** tools for chopping ice or securing oneself while climbing over ice
>
> **porters:** people who carry supplies

>> What happened during Edmund Hillary's historic trek? Complete the summary below by filling in the blanks with words from the box above.

Edmund Hillary's team was trying to make history. The team wanted to be the first to make the _____ climb to the top of Mt. Everest. On March 26, 1953, Hillary arrived with climbers and _____ at Tengpoche Monastery. Then, the team climbed to 17,900 feet and created a _____ as a temporary home. Avoiding dangerous _____, Hillary and teammate Tenzing Norgay were able to reach Camp IV. The first teammates to attempt to reach the _____ were Bourdillon and Evans. When their oxygen system failed, they had to turn back. At Camp IX, the rest of the team headed back down. Hillary and Norgay were left alone to think about the dangerous final leg of the climb. Using _____ on their boots and _____, the two climbers struggled to the top of the mountain. On May 29, 1953, they became the first people in history to reach the "top of the world."

LA.A.1.3.4.7.4 Analyzes information from one textual source to create a report
LA.A.2.3.5.7.1 Uses print and electronic sources to locate relevant information for a given task
LA.A.2.3.5.7.2 Compiles, organizes, and interprets information for a variety of purposes
LA.A.2.3.6.7.1 Gathers information from a variety of sources, including primary sources
LA.A.2.3.6.7.2 Identifies and utilizes information from a variety of sources including primary when researching content area topics

Name _____

Using the Library

>> Look over the Library Resources. Then, tell which resources you would use to find the information items listed.

> To find information in a library, be aware of all the different resources that are available.

Library Resources

☐ **Card Catalogues** are for looking up print and non-print resources by title, author, or subject. Most are computerized.

☐ **Shelves or Stacks** are where a library's books are kept.

☐ **Vertical Files** hold pictures, maps, photographs, brochures, and pamphlets.

☐ **Periodicals** are newspapers and magazines.

☐ **Networked Computers** provide connections to the Internet and access to CD-ROM databases.

☐ **Reference Shelves** contain books such as encyclopedias, dictionaries, and almanacs.

☐ **Audio/Video Resources** include cassettes, records, videotapes, CDs, and DVDs.

1. A photo of a candidate in an election held last week _____

_____

2. A magazine article about endangered species _____

_____

3. A book about endangered species

_____

_____

4. A book-on-cassette by a fiction author

_____

_____

5. A brochure for a local museum

_____

_____

6. A photograph of a sand dune

_____

_____

7. A thesaurus _____

_____

Name _____

Photo-Story

>> Use this page as a worksheet for planning your photo-story. Create additional pages as necessary.

Sample

Photo 1: Photo of Saharan sand dunes

Caption: Introduction describing what deserts are

Photo 1:

Caption:

Photo 2:

Caption:

Photo 3:

Caption:

Photo 4:

Caption:

Photo 5:

Caption:

Photo 6:

Caption:

LA.A.1.3.4.7.4 Analyzes information from one textual source to create a report
LA.A.2.3.5.7.1 Uses print and electronic sources to locate relevant information for a given task
LA.A.2.3.5.7.2 Compiles, organizes, and interprets information for a variety of purposes
LA.A.2.3.6.7.1 Gathers information from a variety of sources, including primary source
LA.A.2.3.6.7.2 Identifies and utilizes information from a variety of sources including primary when researching content area topics

Name _____

Finding Biographical Information

> Use a variety of biographical resources appropriate to each stage of your research.

>> Keep track of the resources that you use to find information for your biographical sketch.

Biographical Resources

☐ **Magazines** are a good resource for profiles and interviews. Search an electronic database or the *Reader's Guide to Periodical Literature* to locate articles.

☐ **Encyclopedias** usually provide overviews of the lives of important people.

☐ **Specialized Encyclopedias** contain entries on people within a specific field such as art, science, or literature.

☐ **Biographical Dictionaries** contain brief articles about notable people.

☐ **Biographies and Autobiographies** provide comprehensive information about people's life stories. In an autobiography, the subject describes life experiences in his or her own words.

☐ **Internet Sites** Web sites exist for almost every notable individual. Make sure the information they provide is reliable.

My Subject: _____

Initial Research: To get a quick overview of my subject's life

Resource 1

Type: _____

Title: _____

Resource 2

Type: _____

Title: _____

In-depth Research: To learn more about my subject's character and find details such as quotes, anecdotes, and examples

Resource 3

Type: _____

Title: _____

Resource 4

Type: _____

Title: _____

LA.A.2.3.5.7.2 Compiles, organizes, and interprets information for a variety of purposes

Name _____

Biographical Sketch

>> Use this page to help you record information for your biographical sketch.

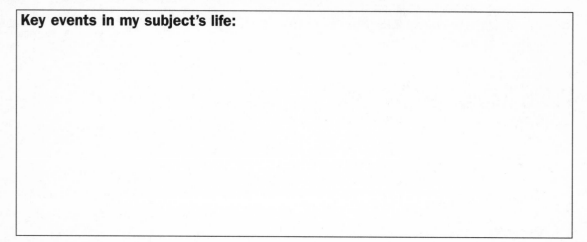

Key events in my subject's life:

Details about the character of my subject:

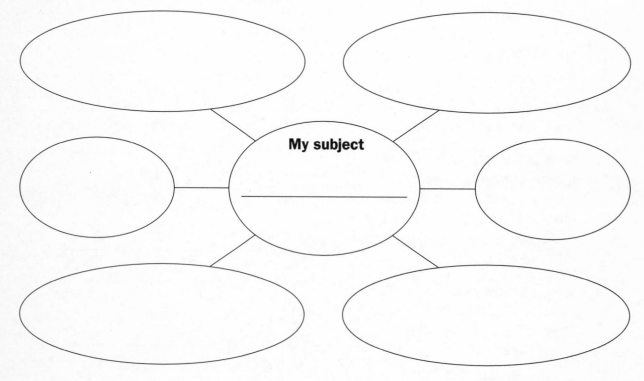

My subject

Write a Biographical Sketch

Name _____

Using a Dictionary

> Dictionaries provide more that just the definition and spelling of a word.

Information Types
1. spelling
2. pronunciation
3. syllabication
4. part of speech
5. etymology/word origins
6. cross references to other words
7. multiple meanings
8. synonyms

(1) (2)(3) (4) (5)

heritage (her´ət ij) n. [ME < Ofr.< heriter < LL. *hereditare*, to inherit < L. *hereditas*: see *HEREDITY*] —(6)
1. property that is or can be inherited
(7) 2. a) something handed down from one's ancestors or the past, such as a culture or tradition, etc. b) the rights, responsibilities, or status resulting from being born in a certain time or place
(8) SYN: **inheritance, birthright, patrimony**

>> Use a dictionary to answer the questions below.

1. How many syllables are in the word *ancestor*? _____

2. Is the word written *bilingual* or *bi-lingual*? _____

3. What part of speech is the word *rural*? _____

4. What is the plural of the word *nationality*? _____

5. What is a synonym for the word *citizen*? _____

6. What are two definitions for the word *proof*? _____

_____

_____

7. What are the guide words on the page for *urban*? _____

_____

Develop an Extended Definition

LA.A.2.3.5.7.2 Compiles, organizes, and interprets information for a variety of purposes

Name _____

Extended Definition

➤➤ Use this page to help you organize information for your Extended Definition.

My Word:

_____

Dictionary Definition:

_____

_____

_____

In the web, list ideas, examples, quotations, or details that extend the meaning of the dictionary definition.

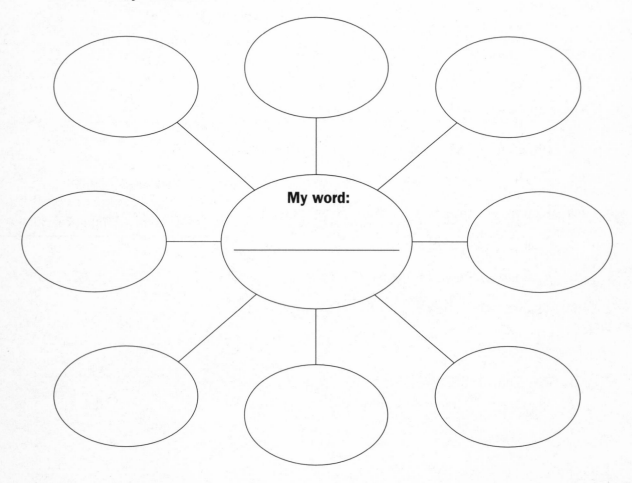

LA.A.1.3.4.7.4 Analyzes information from one textual source to create a report
LA.A.2.3.5.7.1 Uses print and electronic sources to locate relevant information for a given task
LA.A.2.3.5.7.2 Compiles, organizes, and interprets information for a variety of purposes
LA.A.2.3.6.7.1 Gathers information from a variety of sources, including primary sources
LA.A.2.3.6.7.2 Identifies and utilizes information from a variety of sources including primary when researching content area topics

Name _____

Using a Library Catalogue

>> Look at the card. Then, answer the questions.

> Begin your information search at the library catalogue. Search for resources by entering words from the title, author, or subject into the search screen. Or, enter key words.

call number—
where the book or other resource is located in the library using the Dewey Decimal or Library of Congress system

description—
the number of pages and whether or not the resource includes photographs or illustrations

notes—
whether it includes a bibliography or index

CALL #	323.4409 W
AUTHOR	Wright, Roberta Hughes.
TITLE	The birth of the Montgomery bus boycott / Roberta Hughes Wright; with foreword by L. Douglas Wilder, governor of the Commonwealth of Virginia.
PUBLISHER	Southfield, Mich. : Charro Press, c1991.
DESCRIPT	156 p. : ill. ; 22 cm.
NOTES	1) Bibliography: p. 147-150.
SUBJECTS	1) Parks, Rosa, 1913- 2) Segregation in transportation – Alabama – Montgomery. 3) Civil rights demonstrations – Alabama – Montgomery. 4) Afro-Americans – Civil rights – Alabama – Montgomery.

subjects—subjects under which the resource is listed

1. How many pages are in this book? _____

2. What is the publication date? _____

LA.A.2.3.5.7.2 Compiles, organizes, and interprets information for a variety of purposes

Name _____

Informative Poster

>> Use this page to help you brainstorm ideas for your informational poster.

My Topic: _____

Summarize Information to Present:

Sketch Poster Ideas

List Image Possibilities:

LA.A.1.3.4.7.4 Analyzes information from one textual source to create a report
LA.A.2.3.5.7.1 Uses print and electronic sources to locate relevant information for a given ta
LA.A.2.3.5.7.2 Compiles, organizes, and interprets information for a variety of purposes
LA.A.2.3.6.7.1 Gathers information from a variety of sources, including primary sources
LA.A.2.3.6.7.2 Identifies and utilizes information from a variety of sources including primary
when researching content area topics

Name _____

Using a Search Engine

>> What information do you need for your country profile? Use a search engine to research three questions. Record the key words and phrases you used as search terms.

> Before using a search engine, focus your search by creating a question. Create a list of key words from your question. Narrow your search by adding key words or searching by phrase.

Research Question 1: _____

Search Engine Used: _____

Original Search Terms: _____

Revised Search Terms: _____

Did you find information relevant to your question? Explain. _____

_____

Research Question 2: _____

Search Engine Used: _____

Original Search Terms: _____

Revised Search Terms: _____

Did you find information relevant to your question? Explain. _____

_____

Research Question 3: _____

Search Engine Used: _____

Original Search Terms: _____

Revised Search Terms: _____

Did you find information relevant to your question? Explain. _____

_____

Name _____

Oral History

>> Use this page to help you prepare for recording an oral history.

1. Who is my oral history subject? _____

2. What is the subject's country of origin? _____

3. What is the focus of the oral history? What area of my subject's life am I most interested in?

_____

_____

_____

4. What questions am I going to ask?

   • _____

   • _____

   • _____

   • _____

   • _____

   • _____

   • _____

   • _____

5. Where will I record the oral history?

_____

_____

LA.A.1.3.4.7.4 Analyzes information from one textual source to create a report
LA.A.2.3.5.7.1 Uses print and electronic sources to locate relevant information for a given
LA.A.2.3.5.7.2 Compiles, organizes, and interprets information for a variety of purposes
LA.A.2.3.6.7.1 Gathers information from a variety of sources, including primary sources
LA.A.2.3.6.7.2 Identifies and utilizes information from a variety of sources including primary
               when researching content area topics

Name _____

Choosing the Right Source

> What information do you need? Fill in the blanks for each box below.

Choosing the right source can help you to research more efficiently and find the information you are looking for.

Information Sources

☐ **Newspapers** provide up-to-date information. Old issues provide information about events from the past.

☐ **Magazines** provide up-to-date and in-depth coverage of specific issues.

☐ **Almanacs** provide historical or statistical information.

☐ **Atlases** contain map collections and may provide facts and figures.

☐ **Nonfiction Books** include autobiographies and biographies. They provide information about a variety of topics.

☐ **Electronic Databases** can contain CD-ROM encyclopedias, statistical information, photos, and more.

☐ **The Internet** includes Web sites for almost every subject, online versions of print media, and sites for government agencies.

What I'm trying to find:

_____

Where I looked:

_____

_____

What I found:

_____

_____

What I'm trying to find:

_____

Where I looked:

_____

_____

What I found:

_____

_____

Prepare an Oral Presentation

LA.D.1.3.3.7.2 Transfers information gathered and recorded informally into a formal presentation
LA.D.2.3.4.7.1 Selects communication tools that will enhance understanding
LA.D.2.3.4.7.2 Recognizes how the tools of graphics, pictures, color, motion, music, and computer technology affect communication across the media

Name _____

Oral Presentation

>> Use this page as a model for creating a presentation map. Refer to your map while delivering your oral presentation.

Introduction

Point in Journey	Details	Presentation Aid Used?
	• • •	
	• • •	
	• • •	
	• • •	

Conclusion

Prepare an Oral Presentation

Assignment Log

Assignment	Pages	Date Given	Date Due

Assignment Log

Assignment	Pages	Date Given	Date Due

Assignment Log

Assignment	Pages	Date Given	Date Due

Assignment Log

Assignment	Pages	Date Given	Date Due